Preface

Mathematical Olympiads have long stood as a beacon of intellectual challenge and academic rigor, inspiring countless students around the world to engage deeply with the beauty and complexity of mathematics. This book, Mathematical Olympiad Problems and Solutions, Volume 2, is a comprehensive compilation aimed at providing aspiring mathematicians with a robust resource to hone their problem-solving skills and deepen their understanding of mathematical concepts.

The journey to mathematical excellence often begins with curiosity and a passion for problem-solving. For many, it is through the intricate puzzles and thought-provoking questions posed in mathematical competitions that this journey truly takes flight. This book is designed to serve as both a guide and a companion for those embarking on this intellectual adventure.

Objectives of This Book

Our primary objective is to provide a wide array of problems that have appeared in various Mathematical Olympiads, coupled with detailed solutions that illuminate the path to solving them. The problems included span various levels of difficulty, from introductory to highly challenging, catering to a broad spectrum of learners.

We also aim to:

- Enhance Problem-Solving Skills: By working through these problems, readers will develop a strategic approach to tackling mathematical challenges, learning to apply theory in creative and innovative ways.

- Deepen Mathematical Understanding: Each solution is crafted to provide not just the answer, but also a thorough explanation of the underlying principles and methodologies. This approach ensures that readers gain a deeper appreciation and understanding of the subject matter.

- Encourage Persistence and Patience: Problem-solving is an iterative process that requires perseverance. Through this collection, we hope to instill a mindset of resilience and determination, encouraging readers to persist even when faced with difficult problems.

Who is This Book For

This book is intended for:

- **Students Preparing for Olympiads:** Whether you are a beginner or an advanced participant, this book offers a rich resource to help you prepare for competitions.

- **Teachers and Coaches:** Educators will find this book useful for guiding their students through the complexities of Olympiad-level mathematics, providing both problems and solutions that can be used in a classroom setting.

- **Mathematics Enthusiasts:** Anyone with a passion for mathematics will enjoy the intellectual stimulation provided by these problems, as well as the satisfaction of uncovering their solutions.

We extend our heartfelt gratitude to the many mathematicians, educators, and problem-solvers who have contributed to the field of Mathematical Olympiads. Their dedication and creativity have inspired this collection. Special thanks are due to our reviewers and collaborators who provided invaluable feedback and helped refine the content of this book.

We hope that Mathematical Olympiad Problems and Solutions will serve as a valuable tool in your mathematical journey, inspiring you to explore, discover, and excel. May the challenges within these pages ignite your passion for mathematics and lead you to new heights of achievement.

Table of Contents

Chapter 1

Problems

Problem 1. Given a real sequence $\{u_n\} : 1, -2, 3, -4, ..., (-1)^{n+1}n$. Find the mean of the first $2n$ terms of the sequence.

Problem 2. Suppose that $\{u_n\}$ is a geometric sequence. Prove that $u_{n-p+1}u_p = u_1 u_n$ for all positive integers n and p such that $n > p$.

Problem 3. Suppose that $\{u_n\}$ is a geometric sequence such that all of its terms has the same sign. Let u_1 be the first term and q be the common ratio of $\{u_n\}$. Prove that the product of the first nth terms of this sequence is given by $P_n = \sqrt{(u_1 u_n)^n}$.

Problem 4. Given a geometric sequence $\{u_n\}$ with the first term u_1 and the common ratio $q, -1 < q < 1$. Prove that the infinite sum of $\{u_n\}$ is given by $S_\infty = \dfrac{u_1}{1 - q}$.

Problem 5. Convergent sequence has a unique limit.

Problem 6. Every convergent sequence is bounded.

Problem 7. (Monotone Convergence Theorem)

1. An increasing sequence $\{x_n\}$ is convergent if and only if it is bounded above. In this case, we obtain $\lim\limits_{n \to +\infty} x_n = \sup\{x_n : n \in \mathbb{N}\}$.

2. A decreasing sequence $\{x_n\}$ is convergent if and only if it is bounded below. In this case, we obtain

$$\lim_{n \to +\infty} x_n = \inf\{x_n : n \in N\}.$$

3

Problem 8. Given a real sequence $\{u_n\}$ which is defined by

$$u_n = \frac{1}{1!} + \frac{1}{2!} + \ldots + \frac{1}{n!}$$

for all $n \geq 1$. Prove that $\{u_n\}$ is convergent.

Problem 9. Given a real sequence $\{u_n\}$ which is defined by

$$u_n = 1 + \frac{1}{2} + \frac{1}{3} + \ldots + \frac{1}{n}.$$

Prove that $\{u_n\}$ is divergent.

Problem 10. Given a real sequence $\{u_n\}$ which is defined by $u_n = \sqrt{a\sqrt{a\sqrt{a...\sqrt{a}}}}$ (n numbers of square root). Using Monotone Convergence Theorem, prove that $\{u_n\}$ is convergent.

Problem 11. Using Monotone Convergence Theorem, prove that the sequence $\{u_n\}$ which is defined by $u_n = \sin\dfrac{\pi}{2^n}$ is convergent.

Problem 12. Given a real sequence $\{x_n\}$ such that $0 < x_n < 2$ and $x_n\left(3 - x_{n+1}\right) > \dfrac{9}{4}$ for all $n \geq 1$. Prove that $\{x_n\}$ is convergent and find its limit.

Problem 13. Given a real sequence $\{x_n\}$ such that $0 < x_n < 1$ and $x_n > \dfrac{x_{n+1}}{1 - x_{n+1}}$ for all $n \geq 1$. Prove that $\{x_n\}$ is convergent and find its limit.

Problem 14. Given a real sequence $\{x_n\}$ such that $x_{n+1}^2 = ax_n + b$, a, b are real numbers. Suppose that the equation $x^2 = ax + b$ has two positive roots α and β such that $\alpha < \beta$. Assume further that $\alpha \leq x_1 \leq \beta$ and $x_n > 0$ for all $n \geq 1$. Prove that $\{x_n\}$ is convergent and find its limit.

Problem 15. Given a real sequence $\{x_n\}$ and $\{y_n\}$ such that $0 < y_1 < x_1$, $x_{n+1} = \dfrac{x_n + y_n}{2}$ and $y_{n+1} = \dfrac{2}{\dfrac{1}{x_n} + \dfrac{1}{y_n}}$ for all $n \geq 1$. Prove that $\{x_n\}$ and $\{y_n\}$ are convergent and find their limits.

Problem 16. Given two real sequences $\{x_n\}$ and $\{y_n\}$ such that $0 < y_1 < x_1$, $x_{n+1} = \dfrac{x_n + y_n}{2}$ and $y_{n+1} = \sqrt{x_n y_n}$ for all $n \geq 1$. Prove that $\{x_n\}$ and $\{y_n\}$ are both convergent and have the same limit.

Problem 17. Given two real sequences $\{x_n\}$ and $\{y_n\}$ such that $x_1 > y_1 > 0$, $x_{n+1} = \sqrt{x_n y_n}$ and $y_{n+1} = \dfrac{2}{\dfrac{1}{x_n} + \dfrac{1}{y_n}}$ for all $n \geq 1$. Prove that $\{x_n\}$ and $\{y_n\}$ are both convergent.

Problem 18. Given a real sequence $\{x_n\}$ such that $x_1 > 1$ and $x_{n+1} = \dfrac{x_n^2 + 1}{2x_n}$ for all $n \geq 1$. Prove that $\{x_n\}$ is a convergent sequence and find its limit.

Problem 19. (Sandwich Theorem)
Suppose the three real sequences $\{x_n\}, \{y_n\}$ and $\{z_n\}$ satisfying $x_n \leq y_n \leq z_n$ for all $n \geq n_0$, $n_0 \in \mathbb{N}$. If $\lim\limits_{n \to +\infty} x_n = \lim\limits_{n \to +\infty} z_n = l$, prove that $\lim\limits_{n \to +\infty} y_n = l$.

Problem 20. Given a real sequence $\{u_n\}$ such that $u_n = \dfrac{(-1)^n}{n^2}$ for all $n \geq 1$. Find $\lim\limits_{n \to +\infty} u_n$.

Problem 21. Given a real sequence $\{u_n\}$ such that $u_n = \dfrac{n + \sin n^\circ}{n + 1}$ for all $n \geq 1$. Find $\lim\limits_{n \to +\infty} u_n$.

Problem 22. Compute $\lim\limits_{n \to +\infty} \left(\dfrac{n^{m-1}}{n^m + 1} + \dfrac{n^{m-1}}{n^m + 2} + ... + \dfrac{n^{m-1}}{n^m + n} \right)$ for all $m \geq 1$.

Problem 23. Given a real sequence $\{u_n\}$ whose all terms are positive. Suppose that $\lim\limits_{n \to +\infty} \dfrac{u_{n+1}}{u_n} = l$. Prove that

1. If $l < 1$, then $\lim\limits_{n \to +\infty} u_n = 0$.

2. If $l > 1$, prove that $\lim\limits_{n \to +\infty} u_n = +\infty$.

Problem 24. Suppose that $\{x_n\}$ is a real sequence such that $x_n > 0$ for all $n \geq 1$. Find $\lim\limits_{n \to +\infty} x_1 x_2 ... x_n$ if $\lim\limits_{n \to +\infty} x_n = \dfrac{1}{2}$.

Problem 25. (The Stolz-Cesàro Theorem)
Suppose that $\{x_n\}$ and $\{y_n\}$ are two real sequences such that $\{y_n\}$ is increasing to $+\infty$. If $\lim\limits_{n\to+\infty} \dfrac{x_{n+1} - x_n}{y_{n+1} - y_n} = l$, we obtain $\lim\limits_{n\to+\infty} \dfrac{x_n}{y_n} = l$.

Problem 26. Using The Stolz-Cesàro theorem, find $l = \lim\limits_{n\to+\infty} \dfrac{\ln n}{n}$.

Problem 27. Using The Stolz-Cesàro theorem, to find

$$l = \lim_{n\to+\infty} \frac{1^k + 2^k + ... + n^k}{n^{k+1}}$$

for all positive integer k.

Problem 28. Using the Stolz-Cesàro theorem, find

$$l = \lim_{n\to+\infty} \frac{\sqrt{1} + \sqrt{2} + ... + \sqrt{n}}{n\sqrt{n}}.$$

Problem 29. Given a real sequence $\{u_n\}$ converges to l. Prove that

$$\lim_{n\to+\infty} \frac{u_1 + u_2 + ... + u_n}{n} = l.$$

Problem 30. Using the Stolz-Cesàro theorem, find

$$l = \lim_{n\to+\infty} \frac{1}{n}\left(1 + \frac{1}{2} + \frac{1}{3} + ... + \frac{1}{n}\right).$$

Problem 31.   1. For all $x \geq 0$, prove that $\sin x \geq x - \dfrac{1}{6}x^3$.

2. Given a real sequence $\{x_n\}$ such that $x_1 = \dfrac{1}{2}$ and $x_{n+1}^3 = 6x_n - 6\sin x_n$ for all $n \geq 1$. Prove that $\{x_n\}$ is convergent and find its limit.

Problem 32. Suppose that x_1 and x_2 are the two roots of the quadratic equation $x^2 + ax + b = 0$, where $x_1 > x_2 > 0$. Find

$$S = 1 + \left(\frac{x_1}{x_2}\right) + \left(\frac{x_1}{x_2}\right)^2 + ... + \left(\frac{x_1}{x_2}\right)^n + ...$$

Problem 33. (Fermat's Theorem)
Given an integer a. Suppose that p is a prime number such that $p \nmid a$. Then $a^{p-1} \equiv 1 \pmod{p}$.

Problem 34. (Fermat's Little Theorem)
Suppose that p is a prime number. Then $a^p \equiv a \pmod{p}$.

Problem 35. (Wilson's Theorem)
Given a positive integer p. Then $(p - 1)! \equiv -1 \pmod{p}$ if and only if p is prime.

Problem 36. Suppose that a, b and c are the length of the three sides of a triangle. Prove that

$$\sqrt[3]{(p - a)(p - b)(p - c)} \leq \frac{1}{2}\sqrt[3]{abc}.$$

Problem 37. Given a, b and $c \neq 0$ are three real numbers. Suppose that $px + l, qx + m$ and $rx + n$ are the remainders when $Q(x)$ is divided by $(x - a)(x - b), (x - b)(x - c)$ and $(x - c)(x - a)$ respectively. Prove that $\frac{1}{b}(m - l) + \frac{1}{a}(l - n) + \frac{1}{c}(n - m) = 0$.

Problem 38. Let P be the nth degree polynomial such that

$$P(k) = \frac{k - 1}{k + 1}$$

for all $k = \overline{1, n + 1}$. Find $P(n + 3)$.

Problem 39. Given $P(x)$ is a polynomial of degree n such that

$$P(x) = x^n + a_{n-1}x^{n-1} + \dots + a_1 x + a_0$$

, where $a_0, a_1, \dots, a_{n-1}$ are positive real numbers. Suppose that all roots of $P(x)$ are real numbers. Prove that

$$\frac{\left(n^n + a_{n-1}n^{n-1} + \dots + a_1 n + a_0\right)^{n+1}}{(n + 1)^{n(n+1)}} \geq a_0.$$

Problem 40.   1. Given that x_1, x_2 and x_3 are the three roots of $ax^3 + bx^2 + cx + d = 0, a \neq 0$. Let $S_n = x_1^n + x_2^n + x_3^n$ for all $n \geq 0$. Prove that

$$aS_{n+3} + bS_{n+2} + cS_{n+1} + dS_n = 0.$$

7

2. Given a, b and c are three real numbers such that $a + b + c = 1, a^2 + b^2 + c^2 = 3$ and $a^3 + b^3 + c^3 = 5$. Compute $a^4 + b^4 + c^4$.

Problem 41. Suppose that x_1, x_2 and x_3 are the three roots of the cubic equation $x^3 - x^2 + x - 2021 = 0$. Compute

$$S = \frac{(x_1 + x_2)(x_2 + x_3)(x_3 + x_1)}{(1 + x_1)(1 + x_2)(1 + x_3)}.$$

Problem 42. Let a, b and c be the three roots of the cubic equation $P(x) = x^3 - k_1 x^2 + k_2 x - k_3$. Assume that $Q(x) = x^3 + l_1 x^2 + l_2 x + l_3$ has three roots which are $bc - a^2, ca - b^2$ and $ab - c^2$. Prove that

$$\left(k_2^6 + k_2^4 + k_2^2 + 1\right)\left(l_3^2 + l_2^2 + l_1^2 + 1\right) - k_1^2 k_3^2 \geq 0.$$

Problem 43. Compute

$$S = \frac{1}{\cos x \cos 2x} + \frac{1}{\cos 2x \cos 3x} + \ldots + \frac{1}{\cos(n-1)x \cos nx}$$

for all $n \geq 2$.

Problem 44. Suppose that a, b and c are three real numbers such that $a^2 + b^3 + c^4 = 1$. Prove that $a^3 + b^3 + c^3 \leq \sqrt{a^4 + b^3 + c^2}$.

Problem 45. Given the Fibonacci sequence $\{f_n\}$ which is defined by $f_0 = 0, f_1 = 1$ and $f_n = f_{n-1} + f_{n-2}$ for all $n \geq 2$. Prove the following equalities:

1. $f_1 + f_2 + f_3 + \ldots + f_n = f_{n+2} + 1$ for all $n \geq 1$;

2. $f_1 f_4 + f_2 f_5 + f_3 f_6 + \ldots + f_{n-2} f_{n+1} = f_n^2 - 1$ for all $n \geq 2$;

3. $f_1^2 + f_2^2 + \ldots + f_n^2 = f_n f_{n+1}$ for all $n \geq 1$;

4. $f_{n-1} f_{n+1} - f_n^2 = (-1)^n$; for all $n \geq 2$ (Cassini's identity);

5. $x^n = f_n x + f_{n-1}$ for all $n \geq 2$ and x such that $x^2 = x + 1$;

6. $f_n = \frac{1}{\sqrt{5}}\left[\left(\frac{1 + \sqrt{5}}{2}\right)^n - \left(\frac{1 - \sqrt{5}}{2}\right)^n\right]$ (Binet's Formula).

Problem 46. Given the Fibonacci sequence $\{f_n\}$. Compute

$$S = \frac{f_1}{f_2^2 + f_1 f_2} + \frac{f_2}{f_3^2 + f_2 f_3} + \ldots + \frac{f_n}{f_{n+1}^2 + f_{n+1} f_n}.$$

Problem 47. Given the Fibonacci sequence $\{f_n\}$. Prove that

$$C(n,1) f_1 + C(n,2) f_2 + \ldots + C(n,n) f_n = f_{2n}.$$

Problem 48.   1. Compute $\displaystyle\lim_{n\to+\infty} \frac{1^k + 2^k + \ldots + n^k}{n^{k+1}}$.

2. For all real numbers $x > -1$, prove that

$$\frac{x}{l + (l-1)x} \le \sqrt[l]{1+x} - 1 \le \frac{x}{l}$$

, where $l \ge 2$.

3. Compute $\displaystyle\lim_{n\to+\infty} \left(-n + \sum_{k=1}^{n} \sqrt[l]{1 + \frac{k^{l-1}}{n^l}} \right)$ for all $l \ge 2$.

Problem 49. Given a real sequence $\{a_n\}$ such that $a_1 = 1$ and $a_{n+1}^3 = a_n^3 + 3n^2 + 3n + 1$ for all positive integer n.

1. Find the nth term of $\{a_n\}$;

2. Compute $\displaystyle\sum_{k=1}^{n} \frac{1}{a_k (a_k + 1)(a_k + 2)}$.

Problem 50. Let P_n be the product of the first n terms of the sequence $\{a_n\}$. Suppose that $P_n = n!$ for all positive integers n.

1. Find the nth term of $\{a_n\}$.

2. Let $S_n = a_1^4 + a_2^4 + a_3^4 + \ldots + a_n^4$. Find S_n in terms of n.

Problem 51. Given a real sequence $\{u_n\}$ which is defined by

$$u_n = \frac{1}{\sqrt{1}} + \frac{1}{\sqrt{2}} + \ldots + \frac{1}{\sqrt{n}} - 2\sqrt{n} + 2$$

for all positive integers $n \ge 1$. Prove that $\{u_n\}$ is a convergent sequence.

Problem 52. Without using the calculator, prove that

$$\frac{\sin 22° \sin 40°}{\sin 33° \sin 44°} < \frac{20}{33} \left(\frac{\cos 22° \cos 40°}{\cos 33° \cos 44°} \right).$$

9

Problem 53. For all $p \geq 2$, prove that the real sequence $\{u_n\}$ which is defined by $u_n = \dfrac{1}{1^p} + \dfrac{1}{2^p} + \dfrac{1}{3^p} + \ldots + \dfrac{1}{n^p}$ is a convergent sequence.

Problem 54. Given a real sequence $\{u_n\}$ which is defined by $u_1 = \sqrt[k]{a}$ and $u_{n+1} = \sqrt[k]{a + \sqrt[k]{u_n}}$, where $a > 2$. Prove that $\{u_n\}$ is convergent.

Problem 55. Given a real sequence $\{u_n\}$ which is defined by $u_n = \dfrac{n}{a^n}$ for all $n \geq 1$ and $a \geq 2$. Prove that $\{u_n\}$ is convergent and find its limit.

Problem 56. For all positive integers n, prove that

$$\frac{1}{2n+1} < \frac{1}{2} \times \frac{3}{4} \times \ldots \times \frac{2n-1}{2n} < \frac{1}{\sqrt{2n+1}}.$$

Problem 57. For all positive integers $n > 1$, prove that

$$n\left(\sqrt[n]{n+1} - 1 - \frac{1}{n+1}\right) < 1 + \frac{1}{2} + \frac{1}{3} + \ldots + \frac{1}{n} - \frac{n}{n+1}$$

$$< n\left(1 - \frac{1}{\sqrt[n]{n+1}}\right).$$

Problem 58. Prove that $e^x > 1 + x + \dfrac{x^2}{2!} + \ldots + \dfrac{x^n}{n!}$ for all real numbers $x > 0$.

Problem 59. Given n is an odd number such that $n \geq 3$. Prove that

$$\left(1 + x + \frac{x^2}{2!} + \frac{x^3}{3!} + \ldots + \frac{x^n}{n!}\right)\left(1 - x + \frac{x^2}{2!} - \frac{x^3}{3!} + \ldots - \frac{x^n}{n!}\right) \leq 1$$

for all $x \neq 0$.

Problem 60. For all positive integers $n \geq 3$, prove that

$$n^{n+1} > (n+1)^n.$$

Problem 61. 1. Prove that $x - \dfrac{x^2}{2} < \ln(1+x) < x$ for all $x > 0$.

2. Given that $S_n = \ln\left[\left(1 + \dfrac{1}{n^2}\right)\left(1 + \dfrac{2}{n^2}\right)\cdots\left(1 + \dfrac{n}{n^2}\right)\right]$.

Compute $\lim\limits_{n\to+\infty} S_n$.

Problem 62.   1. Prove that

$$\ln(1 + x) < x < -\ln(1 - x)$$

for all $0 < x < 1$.

2. Given that $S_n = \dfrac{a}{n + a} + \dfrac{a}{n + 2a} + \cdots + \dfrac{a}{n + na}$ for all $a > 0$.

Compute $\lim\limits_{n\to+\infty} S_n$.

Problem 63. Given M is a point inside triangle ABC. Let x, y and z be the distance from M to the sides $[BC], [CA]$ and $[AB]$ respectively. Find the minimum value of $x^2 + y^2 + z^2$.

Problem 64.   1. (Van Aubel's Theorem)

Given P is a point inside triangle ABC. $[AP), [BP)$ and $[CP)$ cut sides $[BC], [CA]$ and $[AB]$ at D, E and F respectively. Prove that $\dfrac{AF}{FB} + \dfrac{AE}{EC} = \dfrac{AP}{PD}$.

2. Let I be the center of the inscribed circle of triangle ABC and $[AD)$ is the bisector of $\angle A$. Prove that $\dfrac{AI}{ID} = \dfrac{b + c}{a}$.

Problem 65.   1. (Stewart's theorem)

Given a triangle ABC. Let D be a point on the side $[BC]$. Assume that $BC = a, CA = b, AB = c, AD = d, BD = n$ and $CD = m$. Prove that

$$b^2 n + c^2 m = a(d^2 + mn).$$

2. Let m_a be the length of the median of triangle ABC drawing from vertex A. Prove that $m_a^2 = \dfrac{b^2 + c^2}{2} - \dfrac{a^2}{4}$.

3. Given a triangle ABC inscribed in a circle centering at O with radius R. Let G be the centroid of it. Prove that

$$OG^2 = R^2 - \dfrac{a^2 + b^2 + c^2}{9}.$$

4. Let $[AD)$ be the bisector of $\angle A$ of a triangle ABC. Prove that

$$AD = \frac{\sqrt{bc\left[(b+c)^2 - a^2\right]}}{b+c}.$$

Problem 66. Let K be a point in triangle ABC. $[AK), [BK)$ and $[CK)$ cut sides $[BC], [CA]$ and $[AB]$ at A_1, B_1 and C_1 respectively. Prove that

1. $\dfrac{KA_1}{AA_1} + \dfrac{KB_1}{BB_1} + \dfrac{KC_1}{CC_1} = 1;$

2. $\dfrac{AK}{AA_1} + \dfrac{BK}{BB_1} + \dfrac{CK}{CC_1} = 2.$

Problem 67. Given a triangle ABC. Let a, b, c be the lengths of the three sides and h_a, h_b, h_c be the lengths of heights drawing from vertices A, B and C respectively. Let d_a, d_b and d_c be the lengths from the orthocenter of triangle ABC to the vertices A, B and C respectively. Prove that

$$h_a d_a + h_b d_b + h_c d_c = \frac{a^2 + b^2 + c^2}{2}.$$

Problem 68. Given r and R are the radii of the inscribed circle and the circumscribed circle of triangle ABC. Prove that

$$a + b + c \geq 2\sqrt{3r(r + 4R)}.$$

Problem 69. Given r and R are the radii of the inscribed circle and the circumscribed circle of triangle ABC. Prove that

$$\frac{1}{\sin \dfrac{A}{2}} + \frac{1}{\sin \dfrac{B}{2}} + \frac{1}{\sin \dfrac{C}{2}} \geq 4\sqrt{\frac{R}{r}}.$$

Problem 70. Suppose that m and n are two natural numbers. Let

$$S(m, n) = 1^m + 2^m + 3^m + \ldots + n^m.$$

1. Prove that $C(m+1, 1) S(m, n) + C(m+1, 2) S(m-1, n) + \ldots$
   $$+ C(m+1, m) S(1, n) = (n+1)^{m+1} - (n+1).$$

2. Find $S(1, n)$ and $S(2, n)$ in terms of n.

12

3. For all real numbers k, let $[k]$ be the integer part of k. Compute

$$T_2 = \left[\sqrt{1}\right] + \left[\sqrt{2}\right] + ... + \left[\sqrt{n^2 - 1}\right]$$

and

$$T_3 = \left[\sqrt[3]{1}\right] + \left[\sqrt[3]{2}\right] + ... + \left[\sqrt[3]{n^3 - 1}\right]$$

in terms of n.

4. Let $T_k = \left[\sqrt[k]{1}\right] + \left[\sqrt[k]{2}\right] + ... + \left[\sqrt[k]{n^k - 1}\right]$. Prove that

$$T_k + S(k, n) = n^{k+1}.$$

Problem 71. Given $\alpha \in \mathbb{R}$, $a \in \mathbb{Z}$ and $n \in \mathbb{N}$. Prove that

1. $[a + \alpha] = a + [\alpha]$;

2. $\left[\dfrac{\alpha}{n}\right] = \left[\dfrac{[\alpha]}{n}\right]$.

Problem 72. Given x, y and z are three real numbers. Prove that

1. $2\left([x] + [y] + [z]\right) \leq [x + y] + [y + z] + [z + x]$
$$\leq 2\left([x] + [y] + [z]\right) + 3;$$

2. $2\left([x] + [y] + [z]\right)$
$$\leq 2\left([2x] + [2y] + [2z]\right) - [x + y] - [y + z] - [z + x].$$

Problem 73. For all real numbers x and positive integers n, prove that

1. $\dfrac{n(n + 1)}{2}[x] \leq [x] + [2x] + ... + [nx] \leq \dfrac{n(n + 1)}{2}([x] + 1) - n$;

2. $n + \dfrac{n(n + 1)}{2}(\{x\} - 1) \leq \{x\} + \{2x\} + ... + \{nx\} \leq \dfrac{n(n + 1)}{2}\{x\}$.

Problem 74. Given two positive real numbers α and β which are not an integer. Prove the following inequalities:

1. $\dfrac{\alpha}{\{\alpha\}} + \dfrac{\beta}{\{\beta\}} \geq 2$;

2. $\alpha^2\left(\left[\dfrac{\beta}{\alpha^2}\right] + 1\right) + \beta^2\left(\left[\dfrac{\alpha}{\beta^2}\right] + 1\right) > \alpha + \beta$;

3. $[\alpha][\beta] \leq [\alpha\beta] \leq [\alpha][\beta] + [\alpha] + [\beta]$.

Problem 75. Let $[x]$ be the integer part of x. For all positive integers n, prove that

1. $A = \left[\cos^{2n-1}1°\right] + \left[\cos^{2n-1}2°\right] + ... + \left[\cos^{2n-1}180°\right]$;

2. $B = \left[\sin^{2n-1}1°\right] + \left[\sin^{2n-1}2°\right] + ... + \left[\sin^{2n-1}360°\right]$.

Problem 76. Let $\{x\}$ be the fractional part of x and n be a positive integer. Compute the following sums:

1. $S = \left\{\cos^{2n-1}1°\right\} + \left\{\cos^{2n-1}2°\right\} + ... + \left\{\cos^{2n-1}180°\right\}$;

2. $T = \left\{\sin^{2n-1}1°\right\} + \left\{\sin^{2n-1}2°\right\} + ... + \left\{\sin^{2n-1}360°\right\}$.

Problem 77. Compute the following sums:

1. $S_1 = \left[\dfrac{1^2 + 2^2}{2}\right] + \left[\dfrac{2^2 + 3^2}{2^2}\right] + ... + \left[\dfrac{n^2 + (n+1)^2}{2}\right]$;

2. $S_2 = \left[\dfrac{1^2 + 2^2 + 3^2}{3}\right] + \left[\dfrac{2^2 + 3^2 + 4^2}{3}\right] + ...$

$+ \left[\dfrac{n^2 + (n+1)^2 + (n+2)^2}{3}\right]$.

Problem 78. Given a and b are two integers. Let $[x]$ be the integer part of x. Prove that $\left[\dfrac{a^2 + b^2}{2}\right] + \left[\dfrac{a^2 - b^2}{2}\right]$ does not depend on the choice of b.

Problem 79.   1. Given that k is an integer. Prove that

$$\left[\frac{k}{2}\right] + \left[\frac{k+1}{2}\right] = k.$$

2. Compute $S = \left[\dfrac{1}{2}\right] + \left[\dfrac{2}{2}\right] + ... + \left[\dfrac{n}{2}\right]$.

Problem 80. Suppose that a and b are two real numbers that satisfy $0 \leq a - b \leq 1$. Prove that $[a] - [b] \in \{0, 1\}$.

Problem 81. Let $S_n = 1^m + 2^m + ... + n^m$, where $m \geq 2$ is a positive integer. Find $T_m = \left[\sqrt[m]{1}\right] + \left[\sqrt[m]{2}\right] + ... + \left[\sqrt[m]{n}\right]$ in terms of $\left[\sqrt[m]{n}\right]$ and $S_{\left[\sqrt[m]{n}\right]}$. Then find T_2 and T_3.

14

Problem 82. Compute $S_{m,n} = [\log_m 1] + [\log_m 2] + ... + [\log_m n]$ in terms of $[\log_m n]$. In the above notation, $m \geq 2$ and n are positive integers.

Problem 83. Let x be a real number and n be a positive integer. Prove that

$$[x] + [x + \{x\}] + [2x + \{2x\}] + ... + [2nx + \{2nx\}] = [4nx].$$

Problem 84. Given x is a real number and n is a positive integer. Prove that

$$n(2[x] - 1) \leq \left[x - \frac{1}{n}\right] + \left[x - \frac{1}{n-1}\right] + ... + \left[x + \frac{1}{n-1}\right] + \left[x + \frac{1}{n}\right]$$

$$\leq n(2[x] + 1).$$

Problem 85.   1. (Hermite's identity)
Given x is a real number and n is a positive integer. Prove that

$$[nx] = [x] + \left[x + \frac{1}{n}\right] + \left[x + \frac{2}{n}\right] + ... + \left[x + \frac{n-1}{n}\right].$$

2. Find S which is defined by

$$S = \left[x + \frac{1}{2}\right] + \left[2x + \frac{1}{2}\right] + ... + \left[2^n x + \frac{1}{2}\right].$$

3. For all real number x, prove that

$$\{x\} + \left\{x + \frac{1}{n}\right\} + \left\{x + \frac{2}{n}\right\} + ... + \left\{x + \frac{n-1}{n}\right\} = \{nx\} + \frac{n-1}{2}.$$

Problem 86.   1. Given $x \notin \mathbb{N}$ is a positive real number and $n \geq 2$ is a positive integer. Assume that $\dfrac{1}{\{x\}} \leq n$. Prove that

$$[x] + \left[x + \frac{1}{2}\right] + \left[x + \frac{2}{3}\right] + ... + \left[x + \frac{n-1}{n}\right] = n[x] + n - \left[\frac{1}{\{x\}}\right] + \sigma$$

, where $\sigma = \begin{cases} 1 & \text{if } \dfrac{1}{\{x\}} \in \mathbb{N} \\ 0 & \text{if } \dfrac{1}{\{x\}} \notin \mathbb{N} \end{cases}$.

15

2. Compute $S = [1.2] + \left[1.2 + \dfrac{1}{2}\right] + \left[1.2 + \dfrac{2}{3}\right] + ... + \left[1.2 + \dfrac{99}{100}\right]$.

3. Given $x \notin \mathbb{N}$ is a positive real number such that

$$\frac{1}{\{x\}}, \frac{1}{\{x+0.5\}} \leq 2.$$

Let n be a positive integer. Prove that

$$\left[\frac{1}{\{x\}}\right] + \left[\frac{1}{\{x+0.5\}}\right] + ... + \left[\frac{1}{\{x+0.5n\}}\right]$$
$$= [x] - \left[x + \frac{n+1}{2}\right] + (\sigma + 2)(n+1).$$

Chapter 2

Solutions

Problem 87. Given a real sequence $\{u_n\} : 1, -2, 3, -4, ..., (-1)^{n+1}n$. Find the mean of the first $2n$ terms of the sequence.

Solution. Find the mean of the first $2n$ terms of the sequence. Since $\{u_n\} : 1, -2, 3, -4, ..., (-1)^{n+1}n$, the mean of its first $2n$ terms is defined by

$$\overline{S} = \frac{1 + (-2) + 3 + (-4) + ... + (-1)^{2n+1}2n}{2n}$$
$$= \frac{(1 - 2) + (3 - 4) + ... + (2n - 1 - 2n)}{2n}$$
$$= \frac{\overbrace{-1 - 1 - ... - 1}^{n}}{2n}$$
$$= \frac{-n}{2n}$$
$$= -\frac{1}{2}.$$

Therefore, $\overline{S} = -\dfrac{1}{2}.$

Problem 88. Suppose that $\{u_n\}$ is a geometric sequence. Prove that $u_{n-p+1}u_p = u_1u_n$ for all positive integers n and p such that $n > p$.

Solution. We have

$$u_{n-p+1} = u_1q^{n-p+1-1} = u_1q^{n-p}$$

17

and
$$u_p = u_1 q^{p-1}.$$

It follows that
$$
\begin{aligned}
u_{n-p+1} u_p &= \left(u_1 q^{n-p}\right)\left(u_1 q^{p-1}\right) \\
&= u_1\left(u_1 q^{n-p+p-1}\right) \\
&= u_1\left(u_1 q^{n-1}\right) \\
&= u_1 u_n.
\end{aligned}
$$

Therefore, $u_{n-p+1} u_p = u_1 u_n.$

Problem 89. Suppose that $\{u_n\}$ is a geometric sequence such that all of its terms has the same sign. Let u_1 be the first term and q be the common ratio of $\{u_n\}$. Prove that the product of the first nth terms of this sequence is given by $P_n = \sqrt{(u_1 u_n)^n}$.

Solution. Since $\{u_n\}$ is a geometric sequence, it follows that
$$u_1 u_n = u_2 u_{n-1} = \ldots = u_n u_1.$$

It follows that $P = u_1 u_2 \ldots u_n$. Hence,
$$
\begin{aligned}
P^2 &= \left(u_1 u_2 \ldots u_n\right)\left(u_n u_{n-1} \ldots u_1\right) \\
&= \left(u_1 u_n\right)\left(u_2 u_{n-1}\right) \ldots \left(u_n u_1\right) \\
&= \underbrace{\left(u_1 u_n\right)\left(u_1 u_n\right) \ldots \left(u_1 u_n\right)}_{n \ \text{times of } u_1 u_n} \\
&= \left(u_1 u_n\right)^n.
\end{aligned}
$$

Therefore, $P_n = \sqrt{(u_1 u_n)^n}.$

Problem 90. Given a geometric sequence $\{u_n\}$ with the first term u_1 and the common ratio $q, -1 < q < 1$. Prove that the infinite sum of $\{u_n\}$ is given by $S_\infty = \dfrac{u_1}{1-q}$.

Solution. From the sum of the first n terms of a geometric sequence, we have $S_n = \dfrac{u_1\left(q^n - 1\right)}{q - 1}$. If $-1 < q < 1$, when n is large enough $(n \to +\infty)$, we obtain $q^n \to 0$. Hence,
$$S_\infty = \frac{u_1\left(0 - 1\right)}{q - 1} = \frac{u_1}{1 - q}.$$

Therefore, $S_\infty = \dfrac{u_1}{1-q}$.

Problem 91. Convergent sequence has a unique limit.

Solution. Let $\{u_n\}$ be a given sequence. Suppose that $u_n \to l_1$ and $u_n \to l_2$, where $l_1 \neq l_2$.

- From $u_n \to l_1$, $\forall \varepsilon_1 > 0, \exists N_1 \in \mathbb{N}$ such that

$$|u_n - l_1| < \varepsilon_1 \quad \text{for all } n \geq N_1. \tag{1}$$

- From $u_n \to l_2$, $\forall \varepsilon_2 > 0, \exists N_2 \in \mathbb{N}$ such that

$$|u_n - l_2| < \varepsilon_2 \quad \text{for all } n \geq N_2. \tag{2}$$

From (1) and (2), we obtain

$$
\begin{aligned}
|l_1 - l_2| &= |(l_1 - u_n) + (u_n - l_2)| \\
&\leq |l_1 - u_n| + |u_n - l_2| \\
&= |u_n - l_1| + |u_n - l_2| \\
&< \varepsilon_1 + \varepsilon_2 \quad \text{for all } n \geq \max\{N_1, N_2\}.
\end{aligned}
\tag{3}
$$

Since $l_1 \neq l_2$, it follows that $|l_1 - l_2| > 0$. Hence, we can choose $\varepsilon_1 = \varepsilon_2 = \dfrac{1}{2}|l_1 - l_2|$. (3) becomes $|l_1 - l_2| < \dfrac{1}{2}|l_1 - l_2|$ which is equivalent to $1 < \dfrac{1}{2}$, not true. Thus, the assumption is false.

Therefore, the limit of a convergent sequence is unique.

Problem 92. Every convergent sequence is bounded.

Solution. Suppose that $\{x_n\}$ converges to l. By definition, for all $\varepsilon > 0$, there exists $N \in \mathbb{N}$ such that $|x_n - l| < \varepsilon$ for all $n \geq N$. It follows that $-\varepsilon < x_n - l < \varepsilon$. Then $l - \varepsilon < x_n < \varepsilon + l$ for all $n \geq N$.
Let

$$mi = \min\{x_1, x_2, ..., x_{N-1}, l - \varepsilon\}$$

and

$$ma = \max\{x_1, x_2, ..., x_{N-1}, l + \varepsilon\}.$$

It implies that $mi \leq x_n \leq ma$ for all $n \in \mathbb{N}$. From the last inequality, there exists a real number $M > 0$ such that $|x_n| \leq M$ for all $n \geq 1$.

Therefore, $\{x_n\}$ is bounded.

Problem 93. (Monotone Convergence Theorem)

1. An increasing sequence $\{x_n\}$ is convergent if and only if it is bounded above. In this case, we obtain $\lim\limits_{n \to +\infty} x_n = \sup\{x_n : n \in \mathbb{N}\}$.

2. A decreasing sequence $\{x_n\}$ is convergent if and only if it is bounded below. In this case, we obtain $\lim\limits_{n \to +\infty} x_n = \inf\{x_n : n \in N\}$.

Solution. Suppose that $\{x_n\}$ is increasing.

1. $\Rightarrow$ Assume that $\{x_n\}$ is bounded above. We shall show that $\{x_n\}$ is convergent. Since $\{x_n\}$ is bounded above. Then $\{x_n : n \in \mathbb{N}\}$ has supremum. Let $s = \sup\{x_n : n \in \mathbb{N}\}$. By definition of supremum, for all $\varepsilon > 0$, there exists $N \in \mathbb{N}$ such that $x_N > s - \varepsilon$. By knowing that $\{x_n\}$ is increasing, then $x_n \geq x_N$ for all $n \geq N$. Hence, $s - \varepsilon < x_N \leq x_n \leq s < s + \varepsilon$ for all $n \geq N$. It follows that $|x_n - s| < \varepsilon$ for all $n \geq N$.

   Therefore, x_n converges to $s = \sup\{x_n : n \in \mathbb{N}\}$.

   $\Leftarrow$ Suppose that $\{x_n\}$ is convergent. From Problem 92, we obtain $\{x_n\}$ is bounded.

   Therefore, $\{x_n\}$ is bounded.

   Suppose that $\{x_n\}$ is decreasing.

2. Assume that $\{x_n\}$ is bounded below. We shall show that $\{x_n\}$ is convergent. Since $\{x_n\}$ is bounded below, then $\{x_n : n \in \mathbb{N}\}$ has infimum. Let $f = \inf\{x_n : n \in N\}$. By definition of infimum, for all $\varepsilon > 0$, there exists $N \in \mathbb{N}$ such that $x_N < f + \varepsilon$. By knowing that $\{x_n\}$ is decreasing, then $x_n \leq x_N$ for all $n \geq N$. It follows that $f - \varepsilon < f \leq x_n \leq x_N < f + \varepsilon$. Then $|x - f| < \varepsilon$ for all $n \geq N$. Thus, $x_n \to f$.

   Therefore, $x_n \to f = \inf\{x_n : n \in N\}$.

   $\Leftarrow$ Suppose that $\{x_n\}$ is convergent. From Problem 92, we obtain $\{x_n\}$ is bounded.

   Therefore, $\{x_n\}$ is bounded.

Problem 94. Given a real sequence $\{u_n\}$ which is defined by

$$u_n = \frac{1}{1!} + \frac{1}{2!} + ... + \frac{1}{n!}$$

for all $n \geq 1$. Prove that $\{u_n\}$ is convergent.

Solution. We have $u_n = \dfrac{1}{1!} + \dfrac{1}{2!} + \ldots + \dfrac{1}{n!}$. It follows that

$$u_{n+1} = \dfrac{1}{1!} + \dfrac{1}{2!} + \ldots + \dfrac{1}{n!} + \dfrac{1}{(n+1)!}$$

$$= u_n + \dfrac{1}{(n+1)!}.$$

Then $u_{n+1} - u_n = \dfrac{1}{(n+1)!} > 0$ for all $n \geq 1$.

It turns out that $\{u_n\}$ is an increasing sequence.

Moreover, for all $n \geq 2$, we have

$$u_n = \dfrac{1}{1!} + \dfrac{1}{2!} + \ldots + \dfrac{1}{n!}$$

$$< \dfrac{1}{1!} + \dfrac{1}{1 \times 2} + \ldots + \dfrac{1}{n(n-1)}$$

$$= 1 + \left(1 - \dfrac{1}{2}\right) + \ldots + \left(\dfrac{1}{n-1} - \dfrac{1}{n}\right)$$

$$= 1 + 1 - \dfrac{1}{n}$$

$$= 2 - \dfrac{1}{n} < 2 \quad \text{for all } n \geq 2.$$

Since $u_1 = 1$, we obtain $u_n < 2$ for all $n \geq 1$.

Then $\{u_n\}$ is bounded above.

Therefore, $\{u_n\}$ is convergent.

Problem 95. Given a real sequence $\{u_n\}$ which is defined by

$$u_n = 1 + \dfrac{1}{2} + \dfrac{1}{3} + \ldots + \dfrac{1}{n}.$$

Prove that $\{u_n\}$ is divergent.

Solution. We prove the given statement by contradiction. Suppose that $\{u_n\}$ converges to H. We have

$$H = 1 + \dfrac{1}{2} + \dfrac{1}{3} + \dfrac{1}{4} + \dfrac{1}{5} + \dfrac{1}{6} + \ldots$$

$$= \left(1 + \dfrac{1}{2}\right) + \left(\dfrac{1}{3} + \dfrac{1}{4}\right) + \left(\dfrac{1}{5} + \dfrac{1}{6}\right) + \ldots$$

$$> \left(\dfrac{1}{2} + \dfrac{1}{2}\right) + \left(\dfrac{1}{4} + \dfrac{1}{4}\right) + \left(\dfrac{1}{6} + \dfrac{1}{6}\right) + \ldots$$

$$= 1 + \frac{1}{2} + \frac{1}{3} + \ldots$$

$$= H \text{ , a contradiction.}$$

Therefore, $\{u_n\}$ is convergent.

Problem 96. Given a real sequence $\{u_n\}$ which is defined by $u_n = \sqrt{a\sqrt{a\sqrt{a\ldots\sqrt{a}}}}$ (n numbers of square root). Using Monotone Convergence Theorem, prove that $\{u_n\}$ is convergent.

Solution.   • If $a = 1$, we obtain $u_n = 1$ for all $n \geq 1$. It follows that $\{u_n\}$ is constant. Hence, $\{u_n\}$ is convergent. Furthermore, $u_n \to 1$.

• If $a > 1$, we obtain $u_2 = \sqrt{a\sqrt{a}} > \sqrt{a\sqrt{1}} = \sqrt{a} = u_1$. Suppose that $u_{n+1} > u_n$. We shall show that $u_{n+2} > u_{n+1}$. We have $u_{n+2} = \sqrt{au_{n+1}} > \sqrt{au_n} = u_{n+1}$ for all $n \geq 1$. Hence, $u_{n+1} > u_n$ for all $n \geq 1$. In this case, we obtain $\{u_n\}$ is increasing. Moreover, $u_1 = \sqrt{a} < a$. Suppose that $u_n < a$. It implies that $u_{n+1} = \sqrt{au_n} < \sqrt{a \times a} = \sqrt{a^2} = a$ for all $n \geq 1$. Hence, $u_n < a$ for all $n \geq 1$. Then $\{u_n\}$ is bounded above. Using Monotone Convergence Theorem, we obtain $\{u_n\}$ is convergent.

• If $a < 1$, we obtain $u_2 = \sqrt{a\sqrt{a}} < \sqrt{a} = u_1$. Suppose that $u_{n+1} < u_n$. We shall show that $u_{n+2} < u_{n+1}$. Since $u_{n+1} < u_n$, it follows that $u_{n+2} = \sqrt{au_{n+1}} < \sqrt{au_n} = u_{n+1}$ for all $n \geq 1$. That is, $u_{n+1} < u_n$ for all $n \geq 1$. We obtain $\{u_n\}$ is decreasing. Moreover, $u_n > 0$ for all $n \geq 1$. Then $\{u_n\}$ is bounded below. Hence, $\{u_n\}$ is convergent.

Therefore, $\{u_n\}$ is convergent.

Problem 97. Using Monotone Convergence Theorem, prove that the sequence $\{u_n\}$ which is defined by $u_n = \sin\dfrac{\pi}{2^n}$ is convergent.

Solution. We have $u_n = \sin\dfrac{\pi}{2^n}$.

For all $n \geq 1$, we obtain $0 < \dfrac{\pi}{2^n} \leq \dfrac{\pi}{2}$.

Moreover, $f(x) = \sin x$ is an increasing function on $\left[0, \dfrac{\pi}{2}\right]$. It implies that $\{u_n\}$ is increasing. Furthermore, $u_n = \sin \dfrac{\pi}{2^n} \leq 1$. Then $\{u_n\}$ is bounded above.

Therefore, $\{u_n\}$ is convergent.

Problem 98. Given a real sequence $\{x_n\}$ such that $0 < x_n < 2$ and $x_n (3 - x_{n+1}) > \dfrac{9}{4}$ for all $n \geq 1$. Prove that $\{x_n\}$ is convergent and find its limit.

Solution. Since $0 < x_n < 2$, it follows that $3 - x_{n+1} > 0$ for all $n \geq 1$. Using AM-GM inequality, we obtain

$$x_n + (3 - x_{n+1}) \geq 2\sqrt{x_n (3 - x_{n+1})} > 2\sqrt{\dfrac{9}{4}} = 3.$$

Then $x_{n+1} - x_n < 0$ for all $n \geq 1$.
It implies that $\{x_n\}$ is decreasing.
Moreover, $x_n > 0$ for all $n \geq 1$. Then $\{x_n\}$ is bounded below.

Thus, $\{x_n\}$ is convergent.

Suppose that $x_n \to l$. By knowing that $x_n (3 - x_{n+1}) > \dfrac{9}{4}$, it follows that

$$l (3 - l) \geq \dfrac{9}{4}$$
$$3l - l^2 \geq \dfrac{9}{4}$$
$$12l - 4l^2 \geq 9$$
$$4l^2 - 12l + 9 \leq 0$$
$$(2l - 3)^2 \leq 0.$$

Hence, $2l - 3 = 0$. Then $l = \dfrac{3}{2}$.

Therefore, $x_n \to \dfrac{3}{2}$.

Problem 99. Given a real sequence $\{x_n\}$ such that $0 < x_n < 1$ and $x_n > \dfrac{x_{n+1}}{1 - x_{n+1}}$ for all $n \geq 1$. Prove that $\{x_n\}$ is convergent and find its limit.

Solution. We have $x_n > \dfrac{x_{n+1}}{1 - x_{n+1}}$. It follows that

$$
\begin{aligned}
x_n - x_{n+1} &> \frac{x_{n+1}}{1 - x_{n+1}} - x_{n+1} \\
&= \frac{x_{n+1} - x_{n+1}\left(1 - x_{n+1}\right)}{1 - x_{n+1}} \\
&= \frac{x_{n+1} - x_{n+1} + x_{n+1}^2}{1 - x_{n+1}} \\
&= \frac{x_{n+1}^2}{1 - x_{n+1}}.
\end{aligned}
$$

Since $0 < x_n < 1$, it follows that $x_{n+1}^2 > 0$ and $1 - x_{n+1} > 0$.
Then $x_n - x_{n+1} > 0$ or $x_{n+1} - x_n < 0$. It implies that $\{x_n\}$ is decreasing.
Moreover, $x_n > 0$ for all $n \geq 1$. Then $\{x_n\}$ is bounded below.
Using Monotone Convergence Theorem, it follows that $\{x_n\}$ is convergent.

Therefore, $\{x_n\}$ is convergent.

Suppose that $x_n \to l$. From $x_n > \dfrac{x_{n+1}}{1 - x_{n+1}}$, it follows that

$$
\begin{aligned}
l &\geq \frac{l}{1 - l} \\
1 - l &\geq 1 \\
l &\leq 0.
\end{aligned}
$$

This occurs if and only if $l = 0$.

Therefore, $x_n \to 0$.

Problem 100. Given a real sequence $\{x_n\}$ such that $x_{n+1}^2 = ax_n + b$, a, b are real numbers. Suppose that the equation $x^2 = ax + b$ has two positive roots α and β such that $\alpha < \beta$. Assume further that $\alpha \leq x_1 \leq \beta$ and $x_n > 0$ for all $n \geq 1$. Prove that $\{x_n\}$ is convergent and find its limit.

Solution. We have $\alpha \leq x_1 \leq \beta$. Then $a\alpha + b \leq ax_1 + b \leq a\beta + b$.
Since α and β are the roots of $x^2 = ax + b$, it follows that $a\alpha + b = \alpha^2$
and $\beta^2 = a\beta + b$. Furthermore, $x_{n+1}^2 = ax_n + b$. It follows that

$$
x_2^2 = ax_1 + b.
$$

24

Hence, $\alpha^2 \leq x_2^2 \leq \beta^2$. Then $\alpha \leq x_2 \leq \beta$.

Suppose that $\alpha \leq x_n \leq \beta$. We shall show that $\alpha \leq x_{n+1} \leq \beta$. We obtain

$$\alpha \leq x_n \leq \beta$$
$$a\alpha + b \leq ax_n + b \leq a\beta + b$$
$$\alpha^2 \leq x_{n+1}^2 \leq \beta^2$$
$$\alpha \leq x_{n+1} \leq \beta.$$

Thus, $\alpha \leq x_n \leq \beta$ for all $n \geq 1$.

It turns out that $\{x_n\}$ is bounded.

From $\alpha \leq x_1 \leq \beta$, we obtain $(x_1 - \alpha)(x_1 - \beta) \leq 0$.

It implies that $x_1^2 - (\alpha + \beta) x_1 + \alpha\beta \leq 0$.

By knowing that α and β are the roots of the quadratic equation $x^2 = ax + b$, from Vieta's theorem, we obtain

$$\alpha + \beta = a$$

and

$$\alpha\beta = -b.$$

Then $x_1^2 - ax_1 - b \leq 0$.

It follows that $x_1^2 \leq ax_1 + b = x_2^2$.

As a result, $x_1 \leq x_2$.

Suppose that $x_{n+1} \leq x_n$. We shall show that $x_{n+2} \leq x_{n+1}$.

From $x_{n+1} \leq x_n$, we obtain $ax_{n+1} + b \leq ax_n + b$.

It follows that $x_{n+2}^2 \leq x_{n+1}^2$. Then $x_{n+2} \leq x_{n+1}$.

Hence, $x_{n+1} \leq x_n$ for all $n \geq 1$.

Consequently, $\{x_n\}$ is decreasing.

From Monotone Convergence Theorem, it follows that $\{x_n\}$ is convergent.

$\boxed{\text{Therefore, } \{x_n\} \text{ is convergent.}}$

- If $x_1 = \alpha$, it follows that $x_n = \alpha$ for all $n \geq 1$. In this case, we obtain $x_n \to \alpha$.

- If $x_1 = \beta$, it follows that $x_n = \beta$ for all $n \geq 1$. In this case, we obtain $x_n \to \beta$.

- For the case, $\alpha < x_1 < \beta$, let us suppose that $x_n \to l$. From $x_{n+1}^2 = ax_n + b$, it implies that

$$l^2 = al + b.$$

. Solve the last quadratic equation, we obtain $l \in \{\alpha, \beta\}$. But $\{x_n\}$ is decreasing and $x_n \in (\alpha, \beta)$. Thus, $l = \alpha$. Therefore, $x_n \to \alpha$.

Problem 101. Given a real sequence $\{x_n\}$ and $\{y_n\}$ such that $0 < y_1 < x_1$, $x_{n+1} = \dfrac{x_n + y_n}{2}$ and $y_{n+1} = \dfrac{2}{\dfrac{1}{x_n} + \dfrac{1}{y_n}}$ for all $n \geq 1$.

Prove that $\{x_n\}$ and $\{y_n\}$ are convergent and find their limits.

Solution. Since $0 < y_1 < x_1$, $x_{n+1} = \dfrac{x_n + y_n}{2}$ and $y_{n+1} = \dfrac{2}{\dfrac{1}{x_n} + \dfrac{1}{y_n}}$ for all $n \geq 1$, it follows that $x_n > 0$ and $y_n > 0$ for all $n \geq 1$. Using AM-HM inequality, we obtain

$$x_{n+1} = \frac{x_n + y_n}{2} \geq \frac{2}{\dfrac{1}{x_n} + \dfrac{1}{y_n}} = y_{n+1}.$$

Hence, $x_n \geq y_n$ for all $n \geq 1$.

It follows that $x_{n+1} = \dfrac{x_n + y_n}{2} \leq \dfrac{x_n + x_n}{2} = \dfrac{2x_n}{2} = x_n$ for all $n \geq 1$.

Then $\{x_n\}$ is decreasing. Consequently,

$$\begin{aligned}
y_{n+1} &= \frac{2}{\dfrac{1}{x_n} + \dfrac{1}{y_n}} \\
&= \frac{2x_n y_n}{x_n + y_n} \\
&\geq \frac{2x_n y_n}{x_n + x_n} \\
&= \frac{2x_n y_n}{2x_n} \\
&= y_n \quad \text{for all } n \geq 1.
\end{aligned}$$

Then $\{y_n\}$ is increasing.

It implies that $y_1 \leq y_n \leq x_n \leq x_1$.

Then $\{x_n\}$ and $\{y_n\}$ are both bounded.

Using Monotone Convergence Theorem, it follows that $\{x_n\}$ and $\{y_n\}$ are both convergent.

26

Therefore, $\{x_n\}$ and $\{y_n\}$ are convergent.

Suppose that $x_n \to l_1$ and $y_n \to l_2$. From $x_{n+1} = \dfrac{x_n + y_n}{2}$, we obtain $l_1 = \dfrac{l_1 + l_2}{2}$. It follows that $l_1 = l_2$.

Moreover,

$$x_{n+1}y_{n+1} = \left(\frac{x_n + y_n}{2}\right)\left(\frac{2x_ny_n}{x_n + y_n}\right) = x_ny_n$$

for all $n \geq 1$. Then $x_ny_n = x_1y_1$ for all $n \geq 1$. When $n \to +\infty$, we obtain $l_1 l_2 = x_1 y_1$. It follows that $l_1 l_1 = x_1 y_1$. Hence, $l_1^2 = x_1 y_1$. It implies that $l_1 = l_2 = \sqrt{x_1 y_1}$ since $x_n, y_n > 0$ for all $n \geq 1$.

Therefore, $\{x_n\}$ and $\{y_n\}$ are convergent to $\sqrt{x_1 y_1}$.

Problem 102. Given two real sequences $\{x_n\}$ and $\{y_n\}$ such that $0 < y_1 < x_1$, $x_{n+1} = \dfrac{x_n + y_n}{2}$ and $y_{n+1} = \sqrt{x_ny_n}$ for all $n \geq 1$. Prove that $\{x_n\}$ and $\{y_n\}$ are both convergent and have the same limit.

Solution. We have $0 < y_1 < x_1$, $x_{n+1} = \dfrac{x_n + y_n}{2}$ and $y_{n+1} = \sqrt{x_ny_n}$ for all $n \geq 1$. Then $x_n > 0$ and $y_n > 0$ for all $n \geq 1$. Using AM-GM inequality, we obtain

$$x_{n+1} = \frac{x_n + y_n}{2} \geq \sqrt{x_ny_n} = y_{n+1}.$$

Then $x_n \geq y_n$ for all $n \geq 1$.

Hence, $x_{n+1} = \dfrac{x_n + y_n}{2} \leq \dfrac{x_n + x_n}{2} = x_n$ for all $n \geq 1$.

It follows that $\{x_n\}$ is decreasing.

Moreover, $y_{n+1} = \sqrt{x_ny_n} \geq \sqrt{y_ny_n} = \sqrt{y_n^2} = y_n$ for all $n \geq 1$. It follows that $\{y_n\}$ is increasing. We obtain $x_1 \geq x_n \geq y_n \geq y_1$ for all $n \geq 1$. It implies that $\{x_n\}$ and $\{y_n\}$ are both bounded. Using Monotone Convergence Theorem, we obtain $\{x_n\}$ and $\{y_n\}$ are convergent.

Therefore, $\{x_n\}$ and $\{y_n\}$ are both convergent.

Suppose that $x_n \to l_1$ and $y_n \to l_2$. From $x_{n+1} = \dfrac{x_n + y_n}{2}$, we obtain $l_1 = \dfrac{l_1 + l_2}{2}$. The last equation implies that $l_1 = l_2$.

Therefore, both sequences have the same limit.

Problem 103. Given two real sequences $\{x_n\}$ and $\{y_n\}$ such that $x_1 > y_1 > 0, x_{n+1} = \sqrt{x_n y_n}$ and $y_{n+1} = \dfrac{2}{\dfrac{1}{x_n} + \dfrac{1}{y_n}}$ for all $n \geq 1$.

Prove that $\{x_n\}$ and $\{y_n\}$ are both convergent.

Solution. Since $x_1 > y_1 > 0, x_{n+1} = \sqrt{x_n y_n}$ and $y_{n+1} = \dfrac{2}{\dfrac{1}{x_n} + \dfrac{1}{y_n}}$

for all $n \geq 1$, it follows that $x_n > 0$ and $y_n > 0$.
Using GM-HM inequality, we obtain

$$x_{n+1} = \sqrt{x_n y_n} \geq \frac{2}{\dfrac{1}{x_n} + \dfrac{1}{y_n}} = y_{n+1}.$$

Hence, $x_n \geq y_n$ for all $n \geq 1$.
Then $x_{n+1} = \sqrt{x_n y_n} \leq \sqrt{x_n x_n} = \sqrt{x_n^2} = x_n$ for all $n \geq 1$.
It turns out that $\{x_n\}$ is decreasing. We obtain

$$
\begin{aligned}
y_{n+1} &= \frac{2}{\dfrac{1}{x_n} + \dfrac{1}{y_n}} \\
&= \frac{2x_n y_n}{x_n + y_n} \\
&\geq \frac{2x_n y_n}{x_n + x_n} \\
&= \frac{2x_n y_n}{2x_n} \\
&= y_n \quad \text{for all } n \geq 1.
\end{aligned}
$$

It implies that $\{y_n\}$ is increasing.
Hence, $y_1 \leq y_n \leq x_n \leq x_1$.
Then $\{x_n\}$ and $\{y_n\}$ are both bounded.
Using Monotone Convergence Theorem, we obtain $\{x_n\}$ and $\{y_n\}$ are both convergent.

Therefore, $\{x_n\}$ and $\{y_n\}$ are convergent.

Problem 104. Given a real sequence $\{x_n\}$ such that $x_1 > 1$ and $x_{n+1} = \dfrac{x_n^2 + 1}{2x_n}$ for all $n \geq 1$. Prove that $\{x_n\}$ is a convergent sequence and find its limit.

Solution. We have $x_1 > 1$ and $x_{n+1} = \dfrac{x_n^2 + 1}{2x_n}$ for all $n \geq 1$.

Since $x_n^2 + 1 \geq 2x_n$, we obtain $x_{n+1} \geq \dfrac{2x_n}{2x_n} = 1$.

It follows that $x_n \geq 1$ for all $n \geq 1$.
Then $\{x_n\}$ is bounded below.
Moreover, $x_{n+1} - x_n = \dfrac{x_n^2 + 1}{2x_n} - x_n = \dfrac{x_n^2 + 1 - 2x_n^2}{2x_n} = \dfrac{1 - x_n^2}{2x_n} \leq 0$.
Then $x_{n+1} - x_n \leq 0$ for all $n \geq 1$.
It turns out that $\{x_n\}$ is decreasing.
Using Monotone Convergence Theorem, we obtain $\{x_n\}$ is convergent.

$\boxed{\text{Therefore, } \{x_n\} \text{ is convergent.}}$

Suppose that $x_n \to l$. From $x_{n+1} = \dfrac{x_n^2 + 1}{2x_n}$, it follows that

$$l = \frac{l^2 + 1}{2l}$$
$$2l^2 = l^2 + 1$$
$$l^2 = 1.$$

Then $l = -1$ or $l = 1$.
Hence, $l = 1$ since $x_n \geq 1$ for all $n \geq 1$.
$\boxed{\text{Therefore, } x_n \to 1.}$

Problem 105. (Sandwich Theorem)
Suppose the three real sequences $\{x_n\}, \{y_n\}$ and $\{z_n\}$ satisfying $x_n \leq y_n \leq z_n$ for all $n \geq n_0$, $n_0 \in \mathbb{N}$. If $\lim\limits_{n \to +\infty} x_n = \lim\limits_{n \to +\infty} z_n = l$, prove that $\lim\limits_{n \to +\infty} y_n = l$.

Solution. Since $\lim\limits_{n \to +\infty} x_n = \lim\limits_{n \to +\infty} z_n = l$, then for all $\varepsilon > 0$, there exists $N_1, N_2 \in \mathbb{N}$ such that $|x_n - l| < \varepsilon$ for all $n \geq N_1$ and $|z_n - l| < \varepsilon$ for all $n \geq N_2$. Then $-\varepsilon < x_n - l < \varepsilon$ for all $n \geq N_1$ and $-\varepsilon < z_n - l < \varepsilon$ for all $n \geq N_2$. Let $N = \max\{N_1, N_2, n_0\}$. By knowing that $x_n \leq y_n \leq z_n$ for all $n \geq n_0$, we obtain

$$-\varepsilon < x_n - l \leq y_n - l \leq z_n - l < \varepsilon$$

for all $n \geq N$.
Thus, $|y_n - l| < \varepsilon$ for all $n \geq N$.
$\boxed{\text{Therefore, } y_n \to l.}$

Problem 106. Given a real sequence $\{u_n\}$ such that $u_n = \dfrac{(-1)^n}{n^2}$ for all $n \geq 1$. Find $\lim\limits_{n\to+\infty} u_n$.

Solution. For all $n \geq 1$, we obtain $-1 \leq (-1)^n \leq 1$.

Then $-\dfrac{1}{n^2} \leq \dfrac{(-1)^n}{n^2} \leq \dfrac{1}{n^2}$. By knowing that $\lim\limits_{n\to+\infty}\left(-\dfrac{1}{n^2}\right) = 0$

and $\lim\limits_{n\to+\infty}\dfrac{1}{n^2} = 0$, using Sandwich theorem, we obtain

$$\lim_{n\to+\infty}\frac{(-1)^n}{n^2} = 0.$$

Therefore, $\lim\limits_{n\to+\infty}\dfrac{(-1)^n}{n^2} = 0.$

Problem 107. Given a real sequence $\{u_n\}$ such that $u_n = \dfrac{n + \sin n^\circ}{n+1}$ for all $n \geq 1$. Find $\lim\limits_{n\to+\infty} u_n$.

Solution. For all $n \geq 1$, we have $-1 \leq \sin n^\circ \leq 1$.
Then

$$n - 1 \leq n + \sin n^\circ \leq n + 1.$$

Divide both side of the inequality by $n + 1$, we obtain

$$\frac{n-1}{n+1} \leq \frac{n + \sin n^\circ}{n+1} \leq \frac{n+1}{n+1}.$$

Then

$$\frac{n-1}{n+1} \leq \frac{n + \sin n^\circ}{n+1} \leq 1.$$

By knowing that $\lim\limits_{n\to+\infty}\dfrac{n-1}{n+1} = 1$ and $\lim\limits_{n\to+\infty} 1 = 1$, from Sandwich theorem, we have

$$\lim_{n\to+\infty}\frac{n + \sin n^\circ}{n+1} = 1.$$

Therefore, $\lim\limits_{n\to+\infty}\dfrac{n + \sin n^\circ}{n+1} = 1.$

Problem 108. Compute $\lim\limits_{n\to+\infty}\left(\dfrac{n^{m-1}}{n^m + 1} + \dfrac{n^{m-1}}{n^m + 2} + ... + \dfrac{n^{m-1}}{n^m + n}\right)$ for all $m \geq 1$.

Solution. For all $1 \leq k \leq n$, we obtain

$$\frac{n^{m-1}}{n^m + n} \leq \frac{n^{m-1}}{n^m + k} \leq \frac{n^{m-1}}{n^m + 1}.$$

Then

$$\sum_{k=1}^{n} \frac{n^{m-1}}{n^m + n} \leq \sum_{k=1}^{n} \frac{n^{m-1}}{n^m + k} \leq \sum_{k=1}^{n} \frac{n^{m-1}}{n^m + 1}.$$

It follows that

$$\frac{n \times n^{m-1}}{n^m + n} \leq \sum_{k=1}^{n} \frac{n^{m-1}}{n^m + k} \leq \frac{n \times n^{m-1}}{n^m + 1}.$$

It implies that

$$\frac{n^m}{n^m + n} \leq \sum_{k=1}^{n} \frac{n^{m-1}}{n^m + k} \leq \frac{n^m}{n^m + 1}.$$

By knowing that $\displaystyle\lim_{n \to +\infty} \frac{n^m}{n^m + n} = 1$ and $\displaystyle\lim_{n \to +\infty} \frac{n^m}{n^m + 1} = 1$, from Sandwich theorem, we obatin

$$\lim_{n \to +\infty} \left(\frac{n^{m-1}}{n^m + 1} + \frac{n^{m-1}}{n^m + 2} + \dots + \frac{n^{m-1}}{n^m + n} \right) = 1.$$

Therefore, $\displaystyle\lim_{n \to +\infty} \left(\frac{n^{m-1}}{n^m + 1} + \frac{n^{m-1}}{n^m + 2} + \dots + \frac{n^{m-1}}{n^m + n} \right) = 1.$

Problem 109. Given a real sequence $\{u_n\}$ whose all terms are positive. Suppose that $\displaystyle\lim_{n \to +\infty} \frac{u_{n+1}}{u_n} = l$. Prove that

1. If $l < 1$, then $\displaystyle\lim_{n \to +\infty} u_n = 0$.

2. If $l > 1$, prove that $\displaystyle\lim_{n \to +\infty} u_n = +\infty$.

Solution. Prove that

1. If $l < 1$, then $\displaystyle\lim_{n \to +\infty} u_n = 0$.

   Since $l < 1$, then there exists a positive number $\varepsilon > 0$ such that $l + \varepsilon < 1$. From the hypothesis $\displaystyle\lim_{n \to +\infty} \frac{u_{n+1}}{u_n} = l$, by definition, $\exists N \in \mathbb{N}$ such that $\left| \dfrac{u_{n+1}}{u_n} - l \right| < \varepsilon$ for all $n \geq N$.

We obtain $\dfrac{u_{n+1}}{u_n} < l + \varepsilon$ for all $n \geq N$. It follows that

$$\frac{u_{N+1}}{u_N} < l + \varepsilon$$

$$\frac{u_{N+2}}{u_{N+1}} < l + \varepsilon$$

$$\vdots$$

$$\frac{u_n}{u_{n-1}} < l + \varepsilon.$$

Multiply both sides of the above inequalities, we obtain

$$\frac{u_{N+1}}{u_N} \times \frac{u_{N+2}}{u_{N+1}} \times \dots \times \frac{u_n}{u_{n-1}} < (l + \varepsilon)^{n-N}.$$

Then $\dfrac{u_n}{u_N} < (l + \varepsilon)^{n-N}$.

It implies that $u_n < u_N (l + \varepsilon)^{n-N}$.

By knowing that $l + \varepsilon < 1$, it follows that

$$\lim_{n \to +\infty} (l + \varepsilon)^{n-N} = 0.$$

Then $\lim\limits_{n \to +\infty} u_n = 0$.

Therefore, $\lim\limits_{n \to +\infty} u_n = 0.$

2. If $l > 1$, then $\lim\limits_{n \to +\infty} u_n = +\infty$.

Since $l > 1$, then there exists $\varepsilon > 0$ such that $l - \varepsilon > 1$. We know that $\lim\limits_{n \to +\infty} \dfrac{u_{n+1}}{u_n} = l$, by definition, $\exists N \in \mathbb{N}$ such that $\left| \dfrac{u_{n+1}}{u_n} - l \right| < \varepsilon$ for all $n \geq N$. We obtain $\dfrac{u_{n+1}}{u_n} - l > \varepsilon$. Then $\dfrac{u_{n+1}}{u_n} > l - \varepsilon$ for all $n \geq N$. It implies that

$$\frac{u_{N+1}}{u_N} > l - \varepsilon$$

$$\frac{u_{N+1}}{u_N} > l - \varepsilon$$

$$\vdots$$

$$\frac{u_{n+1}}{u_n} > l - \varepsilon.$$

Multiply all of the above inequalities, we obtain

$$\frac{u_{N+1}}{u_N} \times \frac{u_{N+2}}{u_{N+1}} \times \dots \times \frac{u_{n+1}}{u_n} > (l - \varepsilon)^{n-N}.$$

Then $\dfrac{u_{n+1}}{u_N} > (l - \varepsilon)^{n-N}$. It follows that $u_{n+1} > u_N(l - \varepsilon)^{n-N}$.
By knowing $\lim\limits_{n \to +\infty} u_N(l - \varepsilon)^{n-N} = +\infty$, we obtain

$$\lim_{n \to +\infty} u_n = +\infty.$$

Therefore, $\lim\limits_{n \to +\infty} u_n = +\infty.$

Problem 110. Suppose that $\{x_n\}$ is a real sequence such that $x_n > 0$ for all $n \geq 1$. Find $\lim\limits_{n \to +\infty} x_1 x_2 ... x_n$ if $\lim\limits_{n \to +\infty} x_n = \dfrac{1}{2}$.

Solution. Let $\{u_n\}$ be a sequence such that $u_n = x_1 x_2 ... x_n$. Then $u_n > 0$ for all $n \geq 1$. It follows that

$$\begin{aligned}
\lim_{n \to +\infty} \frac{u_{n+1}}{u_n} &= \lim_{n \to +\infty} \frac{x_1 x_2 ... x_n x_{n+1}}{x_1 x_2 ... x_n} \\
&= \lim_{n \to +\infty} x_{n+1} \\
&= \lim_{n \to +\infty} x_n \\
&= \frac{1}{2} < 1
\end{aligned}$$

From Problem 109, we obtain $\lim\limits_{n \to +\infty} x_1 x_2 ... x_n = 0$.

Therefore, $\lim\limits_{n \to +\infty} x_1 x_2 ... x_n = 0.$

Problem 111. (The Stolz-Cesàro Theorem)
Suppose that $\{x_n\}$ and $\{y_n\}$ are two real sequences such that $\{y_n\}$ is increasing to $+\infty$. If $\lim\limits_{n \to +\infty} \dfrac{x_{n+1} - x_n}{y_{n+1} - y_n} = l$, we obtain $\lim\limits_{n \to +\infty} \dfrac{x_n}{y_n} = l$.

33

Solution. Since $\lim\limits_{n \to +\infty} \dfrac{x_{n+1} - x_n}{y_{n+1} - y_n} = l$, by definition, $\forall \varepsilon > 0, \exists N \in$

$\mathbb{N}$ such that $\left| \dfrac{x_{n+1} - x_n}{y_{n+1} - y_n} - l \right| < \varepsilon$ for all $n \geq N$. It follows that

$$-\varepsilon < \frac{x_{n+1} - x_n}{y_{n+1} - y_n} - l < \varepsilon.$$

Then $l - \varepsilon < \dfrac{x_{n+1} - x_n}{y_{n+1} - y_n} < l + \varepsilon$. We know that $\{y_n\}$ is increasing, then $y_{n+1} - y_n > 0$ for all $n \geq 1$. Hence, for all $n \geq N$, we obtain

$$(l - \varepsilon)(y_{n+1} - y_n) < x_{n+1} - x_n < (l + \varepsilon)(y_{n+1} - y_n).$$

For all $k \geq N$, we obtain

$$(l - \varepsilon) \sum_{n=N}^{k} (y_{n+1} - y_n) < \sum_{n=N}^{k} (x_{n+1} - x_n) < (l + \varepsilon) \sum_{n=N}^{k} (y_{n+1} - y_n)$$

$$(l - \varepsilon)(y_{k+1} - y_N) < x_{k+1} - x_N < (l + \varepsilon)(y_{k+1} - y_N)$$

$$(l - \varepsilon)(y_{k+1} - y_N) + x_N < x_{k+1} < (l + \varepsilon)(y_{k+1} - y_N) + x_N$$

$$\frac{(l - \varepsilon)(y_{k+1} - y_N) + x_N}{y_{k+1}} < \frac{x_{k+1}}{y_{k+1}} < \frac{(l + \varepsilon)(y_{k+1} - y_N) + x_N}{y_{k+1}}$$

$$(l - \varepsilon)\left(1 - \frac{y_N}{y_{k+1}}\right) + \frac{x_N}{y_{k+1}} < \frac{x_{k+1}}{y_{k+1}} < (l + \varepsilon)\left(1 - \frac{y_N}{y_{k+1}}\right) + \frac{x_N}{y_{k+1}}.$$

It implies that

$$\lim_{k \to +\infty} \left[(l - \varepsilon)\left(1 - \frac{y_N}{y_{k+1}}\right) + \frac{x_N}{y_{k+1}}\right]$$

$$< \lim_{k \to +\infty} \frac{x_{k+1}}{y_{k+1}}$$

$$< \lim_{k \to +\infty} \left[(l + \varepsilon)\left(1 - \frac{y_N}{y_{k+1}}\right) + \frac{x_N}{y_{k+1}}\right].$$

Since x_N and y_N are constant, then

$$\lim_{k \to +\infty} \frac{x_N}{y_{k+1}} = 0$$

and

$$\lim_{k \to +\infty} \frac{y_N}{y_{k+1}} = 0.$$

Then $l - \varepsilon < \lim\limits_{k \to +\infty} \dfrac{x_{k+1}}{y_{k+1}} < l + \varepsilon$ for all $\varepsilon > 0$.

Hence, $\lim\limits_{k \to +\infty} \dfrac{x_{k+1}}{y_{k+1}} = l$.

$$\boxed{\text{Therefore, } \lim\limits_{n \to +\infty} \dfrac{x_n}{y_n} = l.}$$

Problem 112. Using The Stolz-Cesàro theorem, find $l = \lim\limits_{n \to +\infty} \dfrac{\ln n}{n}$.

Solution. We have $\{y_n\}$ which is defined by $y_n = n$ increases to $+\infty$. Using The Stolz-Cesàro theorem, we obtain

$$
\begin{aligned}
l &= \lim_{n \to +\infty} \frac{\ln n}{n} \\
&= \lim_{n \to +\infty} \frac{\ln (n+1) - \ln n}{(n+1) - n} \\
&= \lim_{n \to +\infty} \frac{\ln \left(\dfrac{n+1}{n} \right)}{1} \\
&= \lim_{n \to +\infty} \ln \left(\frac{n+1}{n} \right) \\
&= \ln 1 = 0.
\end{aligned}
$$

$$\boxed{\text{Therefore, } l = 0.}$$

Problem 113. Using The Stolz-Cesàro theorem, to find

$$l = \lim_{n \to +\infty} \frac{1^k + 2^k + ... + n^k}{n^{k+1}}$$

for all positive integer k.

Solution. We have $\{y_n\}$ which is defined by $y_n = n^{k+1}$ increases to $+\infty$. Using The Stolz-Cesàro theorem, we obtain

$$
\begin{aligned}
l &= \lim_{n \to +\infty} \frac{1^k + 2^k + ... + n^k}{n^{k+1}} \\
&= \lim_{n \to +\infty} \frac{\left[1^k + 2^k + ... + (n+1)^k \right] - \left(1^k + 2^k + ... + n^k \right)}{(n+1)^{k+1} - n^{k+1}} \\
&= \lim_{n \to +\infty} \frac{(n+1)^k}{(n+1)^{k+1} - n^{k+1}}
\end{aligned}
$$

$$= \lim_{n \to +\infty} \frac{n^k + C\,(k,1)\,n^{k-1} + \ldots + C\,(k,k)}{(k+1)\,n^k + \ldots + C\,(k+1,k+1)}$$

$$= \lim_{n \to +\infty} \frac{n^k}{(k+1)\,n^k}$$

$$= \frac{1}{k+1}.$$

Therefore, $l = \dfrac{1}{k+1}$.

Problem 114. Using the Stolz-Cesàro theorem, find

$$l = \lim_{n \to +\infty} \frac{\sqrt{1} + \sqrt{2} + \ldots + \sqrt{n}}{n\sqrt{n}}.$$

Solution. The sequence $\{y_n\}$ which is defined by $y_n = n\sqrt{n}$ increases to $+\infty$. Using the Stolz-Cesàro theorem, we obtain

$$l = \lim_{n \to +\infty} \frac{\left(\sqrt{1} + \sqrt{2} + \ldots + \sqrt{n+1}\right) - \left(\sqrt{1} + \sqrt{2} + \ldots + \sqrt{n}\right)}{(n+1)\sqrt{n+1} - n\sqrt{n}}$$

$$= \lim_{n \to +\infty} \frac{\sqrt{n+1}}{(n+1)\sqrt{n+1} - n\sqrt{n}}$$

$$= \lim_{n \to +\infty} \frac{\sqrt{n+1}\left[(n+1)\sqrt{n+1} + n\sqrt{n}\right]}{\left[(n+1)\sqrt{n+1}\right]^2 - \left(n\sqrt{n}\right)^2}$$

$$= \lim_{n \to +\infty} \frac{(n+1)^2 + n\sqrt{n\,(n+1)}}{(n+1)^3 - n^3}$$

$$= \lim_{n \to +\infty} \frac{n^2 + 2n + 1 + n^2\sqrt{1 + \dfrac{1}{n}}}{n^3 + 3n^2 + 3n + 1 - n^3}$$

$$= \lim_{n \to +\infty} \frac{n^2 + 2n + 1 + n^2\sqrt{1 + \dfrac{1}{n}}}{3n^2 + 3n + 1}$$

$$= \frac{1+1}{3}$$

$$= \frac{2}{3}.$$

Therefore, $l = \dfrac{2}{3}$.

36

Problem 115. Given a real sequence $\{u_n\}$ converges to l. Prove that

$$\lim_{n \to +\infty} \frac{u_1 + u_2 + \ldots + u_n}{n} = l.$$

Solution. The sequence $\{y_n\}$ which is defined by $y_n = n$ increases to $+\infty$. Using the Stolz-Cesàro theorem, we obtain

$$\lim_{n \to +\infty} \frac{u_1 + u_2 + \ldots + u_n}{n}$$

$$= \lim_{n \to +\infty} \frac{(u_1 + u_2 + \ldots + u_{n+1}) - (u_1 + u_2 + \ldots + u_n)}{n + 1 - n}$$

$$= \lim_{n \to +\infty} \frac{u_{n+1}}{1}$$

$$= \lim_{n \to +\infty} u_{n+1}$$

$$= l.$$

Therefore, $\displaystyle \lim_{n \to +\infty} \frac{u_1 + u_2 + \ldots + u_n}{n} = l.$

Problem 116. Using the Stolz-Cesàro theorem, find

$$l = \lim_{n \to +\infty} \frac{1}{n} \left(1 + \frac{1}{2} + \frac{1}{3} + \ldots + \frac{1}{n} \right).$$

Solution. The sequence $\{y_n\}$ which is defined by $y_n = n$ increases to $+\infty$. Using the Stolz-Cesàro theorem, we obtain

$$l = \lim_{n \to +\infty} \frac{\left(1 + \frac{1}{2} + \frac{1}{3} + \ldots + \frac{1}{n+1} \right) - \left(1 + \frac{1}{2} + \frac{1}{3} + \ldots + \frac{1}{n} \right)}{n + 1 - n}$$

$$= \lim_{n \to +\infty} \frac{\frac{1}{n+1}}{1}$$

$$= \lim_{n \to +\infty} \frac{1}{n + 1}$$

$$= 0.$$

Therefore, $l = 0.$

Problem 117. 1. For all $x \geq 0$, prove that $\sin x \geq x - \dfrac{1}{6}x^3$.

2. Given a real sequence $\{x_n\}$ such that $x_1 = \dfrac{1}{2}$ and $x_{n+1}^3 = 6x_n - 6\sin x_n$ for all $n \geq 1$. Prove that $\{x_n\}$ is convergent and find its limit.

Solution.   1. Prove that $\sin x \geq x - \dfrac{1}{6}x^3$.

Let $f(x) = \sin x - x + \dfrac{1}{6}x^3$.

Then $f'(x) = \cos x - 1 + \dfrac{1}{2}x^2$.

It follows that $f''(x) = -\sin x + x$.

By knowing that $x \geq \sin x$ for all $x \geq 0$, we obtain $f''(x) \geq 0$ for all $x \geq 0$. In this case, we obtain f' is increasing.

Then $f'(x) \geq f'(0) = \cos 0 - 1 + \dfrac{1}{2}\left(0^2\right) = 0$ for all $x \geq 0$.

Hence, f is increasing.

It follows that $f(x) \geq f(0)$ for all $x \geq 0$.

Then $\sin x - x + \dfrac{1}{6}x^3 \geq \sin 0 - 0 + \dfrac{1}{6}\left(0^3\right) = 0$ for all $x \geq 0$.

$\boxed{\text{Therefore, } \sin x \geq x - \dfrac{1}{6}x^3 \text{ for all } x \geq 0.}$

2. Prove that $\{x_n\}$ is convergent and find its limit.

Since $x_1 = \dfrac{1}{2} > 0$ and $x_{n+1}^3 = 6x_n - 6\sin x_n$ for all $n \geq 1$, using mathematical inductions, we obtain $x_n > 0$ for all $n \geq 1$. Applying the inequality in 1, it implies that

$$\sin x_n \geq x_n - \frac{1}{6}x_n^3.$$

Hence, $x_n^3 \geq 6(x_n - \sin x_n) = x_{n+1}^3$.

Then $x_n \geq x_{n+1}$ for all $n \geq 1$.

It implies that $\{x_n\}$ is decreasing.

$\{x_n\}$ is bounded below since $x_n > 0$ for all $n \geq 1$.

Using Monotone Convergence Theorem, we obtain $\{x_n\}$ is convergent.

$\boxed{\text{Thus, } \{x_n\} \text{ is convergent.}}$

Suppose that $x_n \to l$. From $x_{n+1}^3 = 6x_n - 6\sin x_n$, it follows that $l^3 = 6l - \sin l$. Then $\sin l = l - \dfrac{1}{6}l^3$. The last equation occur if and only if $l = 0$.

$\boxed{\text{Therefore, } x_n \to 0.}$

Problem 118. Suppose that x_1 and x_2 are the two roots of the quadratic equation $x^2 + ax + b = 0$, where $x_1 > x_2 > 0$. Find

$$S = 1 + \left(\frac{x_1}{x_2}\right) + \left(\frac{x_1}{x_2}\right)^2 + \ldots + \left(\frac{x_1}{x_2}\right)^n + \ldots$$

Solution. $S = 1 + \left(\frac{x_1}{x_2}\right) + \left(\frac{x_1}{x_2}\right)^2 + \ldots + \left(\frac{x_1}{x_2}\right)^n + \ldots$ is the infinite sum of the geometric sequence with $u_1 = 1$ and common ratio $q = \dfrac{x_1}{x_2}$.

By knowing that $x_1 > x_2 > 0$, we obtain $0 < q < 1$.
It follows that

$$S = \frac{u_1}{1 - q}$$
$$= \frac{1}{1 - \dfrac{x_1}{x_2}}$$
$$= \frac{x_2}{x_2 - x_1}$$

Let $S' = \dfrac{x_1}{x_2 - x_1}$. Then $S, S' < 0$ and

$$S - S' = \frac{x_2}{x_2 - x_1} - \frac{x_1}{x_2 - x_1}$$
$$= \frac{x_2 - x_1}{x_2 - x_1}$$
$$= 1.$$

It implies that

$$S' = S - 1. \tag{1}$$

Moreover,

$$SS' = \frac{x_2 x_1}{(x_2 - x_1)^2}$$
$$= \frac{x_1 x_2}{x_2^2 - 2x_2 x_1 + x_1^2}$$
$$= \frac{x_1 x_2}{(x_1 + x_2)^2 - 4x_1 x_2}.$$

Since x_1 and x_2 are the two roots of the quadratic equation $x^2 + ax + b = 0$, we obtain $x_1 + x_2 = -a$ and $x_1 x_2 = b$. Then

$$SS' = \frac{b}{(-a)^2 - 4b} = \frac{b}{a^2 - 4b}. \tag{2}$$

From (1) and (2), we obtain

$$S(S-1) = \frac{b}{a^2 - 4b}$$

$$S^2 - S - \frac{b}{a^2 - 4b} = 0.$$

The discriminant of the last quadratic equation is defined by

$$\Delta = 1 + \frac{4b}{a^2 - 4b}$$
$$= \frac{a^2 - 4b + 4b}{a^2 - 4b}$$
$$= \frac{a^2}{a^2 - 4b}.$$

The equation has two distinct roots. They are

$$S_1 = \frac{1 + \sqrt{\dfrac{a^2}{a^2 - 4b}}}{2} = \frac{1}{2} + \frac{1}{2} \frac{|a|}{\sqrt{a^2 - 4b}}$$

and

$$S_2 = \frac{1}{2} - \frac{1}{2} \frac{|a|}{\sqrt{a^2 - 4b}} < 0.$$

Therefore, $S = \dfrac{1}{2} - \dfrac{1}{2} \dfrac{|a|}{\sqrt{a^2 - 4b}}.$

Problem 119. (Fermat's Theorem)
Given an integer a. Suppose that p is a prime number such that $p \nmid a$. Then $a^{p-1} \equiv 1 \pmod{p}$.

Solution. We see that $a, 2a, 3a, ..., (p-1)a$ are not zero modulo p since $\gcd(x, p) = 1$ for all $x = \overline{1, p-1}$ and $x = a$. Moreover, they are all distinct modulo p. Why this is the case?
Suppose that $ka \equiv la \pmod{p}$, where $1 \le k < l \le p-1$.

Then $k \equiv l \pmod{p}$ cannot be the case.

Hence, $a, 2a, 3a, ..., (p-1)a$ are the same as $1, 2, 3, ..., p-1$ in some order modulo p. It follows that

$$a \times 2a \times 3a \times ... \times (p-1)a \equiv 1 \times 2 \times 3 \times ... \times (p-1) \pmod{p}$$

or

$$a^{p-1}(p-1)! \equiv (p-1)! \pmod{p}.$$

By knowing that $\gcd(p, (p-1)!) = 1$, we obtain $a^{p-1} \equiv 1 \pmod{p}$.

$\boxed{\text{Therefore, } a^{p-1} \equiv 1 \pmod{p}.}$

Problem 120. (Fermat's Little Theorem)
Suppose that p is a prime number. Then $a^p \equiv a \pmod{p}$.

Solution.   • If $p \mid a$, then $a^p \equiv a \pmod{p}$, true.

   • If $p \nmid a$, from Fermat's theorem, we obtain $a^{p-1} \equiv 1 \pmod{p}$. Multiply both sides of the last congruence by a, we obtain $a^p \equiv a \pmod{p}$.

$\boxed{\text{Therefore, } a^p \equiv a \pmod{p}.}$

Problem 121. (Wilson's Theorem)
Given a positive integer p. Then $(p-1)! \equiv -1 \pmod{p}$ if and only if p is prime.

Solution. $\Rightarrow$ Suppose that $(p-1)! \equiv -1 \pmod{p}$. We shall show that p is a prime number. We will prove this statement by using mathematical induction. Let us assume that p is composite. Then p has a prime divisor, d, where $1 \le d \le p-1$. We obtain $(p-1)! \equiv 0 \pmod{d}$. From the hypothesis, $(p-1)! \equiv -1 \pmod{p}$. It turns out that $(p-1)! \equiv -1 \pmod{d}$, impossible. Hence, p is a prime number.

$\Leftarrow$ Suppose that p is a prime number. It is obvious to see that the statement holds for $p = 2, 3$. Next, we shall show that the statement still holds for $p > 3$. Since p is a prime number, then it has a primitive root. Let g be a primitive root modulo p. Then $1, g, g^2, ..., g^{p-2}$ are the same modulo p to $1, 2, ..., p-1$ respectively. Then

$$(p-1)! \equiv 1gg^2...g^{p-2} \equiv g^{1+2+...+(p-2)} \pmod{p}.$$

41

By knowing that $1 + 2 + ... + (p-2) = \dfrac{(p-2)\,(p-1)}{2}$, it follows that

$$(p-1)! \equiv g^{\frac{(p-2)(p-1)}{2}} \pmod{p}.$$

Since p is an odd prime, then $p = 2k + 1$ for some positive integer k.

Then $k < 2k = p - 1$. It follows that $g^k \not\equiv 1 \pmod{p}$.

From Fermat's theorem, we obtain $g^{2k} = g^{p-1} \equiv 1 \pmod{p}$.

Since $\left(g^k\right)^2 = g^{2k} \equiv 1 \pmod{p}$, then $g^k \equiv \pm 1 \pmod{p}$. As a result, $g^k \equiv -1 \pmod{p}$. Therefore,

$$\begin{aligned}
(p-1)! &= g^{\frac{(p-2)(p-1)}{2}} \\
&= g^{k(2k-1)} \\
&= \left(g^k\right)^{2k-1} \\
&\equiv (-1)^{2k-1} \\
&\equiv -1 \pmod{p}.
\end{aligned}$$

Therefore, $(p-1)! \equiv -1 \pmod{p}$ if and only p is a prime number.

Problem 122. Suppose that a, b and c are the length of the three sides of a triangle. Prove that

$$\sqrt[3]{(p-a)\,(p-b)\,(p-c)} \le \frac{1}{2}\sqrt[3]{abc}.$$

Solution. Prove that $\sqrt[3]{(p-a)\,(p-b)\,(p-c)} \le \dfrac{1}{2}\sqrt[3]{abc}$.

The given inequality is equivalent to

$$(p-a)\,(p-b)\,(p-c) \le \frac{1}{8}abc.$$

Since $2p = a + b + c$, it follows that

$$(a+b-c)\,(b+c-a)\,(c+a-b) \le abc.$$

Let $x = a + b - c$, $y = b + c - a$ and $z = c + a - b$.

Since a, b and c are the lengths of the three sides of triangle ABC, we obtain

$$\begin{cases} a + b - c > 0 \\ b + c - a > 0 \\ c + a - b > 0 \end{cases}.$$

42

Then x, y and $z > 0$.

Furthermore, $a = \dfrac{x+z}{2}, b = \dfrac{x+y}{2}$ and $c = \dfrac{y+z}{2}$.

The given inequality is equivalent to

$$xyz \le \left(\frac{x+y}{2}\right)\left(\frac{y+z}{2}\right)\left(\frac{z+x}{2}\right). \tag{1}$$

To prove the given inequality, it is sufficient to prove that (1) holds. Using AM-GM, we obtain

$$\frac{x+y}{2} \ge \sqrt{xy};$$

$$\frac{y+z}{2} \ge \sqrt{yz};$$

and $\quad \dfrac{z+x}{2} \ge \sqrt{zx}.$

Multiply all of the above inequalities, we obtain

$$\left(\frac{x+y}{2}\right)\left(\frac{y+z}{2}\right)\left(\frac{z+x}{2}\right) \ge \left(\sqrt{xy}\right)\left(\sqrt{yz}\right)\left(\sqrt{zx}\right)$$

$$= \sqrt{x^2 y^2 z^2}$$

$$= xyz$$

Hence, (1) holds.

$$\boxed{\text{Therefore, } \sqrt[3]{(p-a)(p-b)(p-c)} \le \frac{1}{2}\sqrt[3]{abc}.}$$

Problem 123. Given a, b and $c \ne 0$ are three real numbers. Suppose that $px+l$, $qx+m$ and $rx+n$ are the remainders when $Q(x)$ is divided by $(x-a)(x-b)$, $(x-b)(x-c)$ and $(x-c)(x-a)$ respectively. Prove that $\dfrac{1}{b}(m-l) + \dfrac{1}{a}(l-n) + \dfrac{1}{c}(n-m) = 0$.

Solution. Prove that $\dfrac{1}{b}(m-l) + \dfrac{1}{a}(l-n) + \dfrac{1}{c}(n-m) = 0$.

From the hypothesis, we have

$$Q(x) = (x-a)(x-b)k_1(x) + px + l;$$

$$Q(x) = (x-b)(x-c)k_2(x) = qx + m;$$

and $\quad Q(x) = (x-c)(x-a)k_3(x) + rx + n.$

$$\text{Then } \begin{cases} Q(a) = pa + l = ra + n \\ Q(b) = pb + l = qb + m \\ Q(c) = qc + m = rc + n \end{cases}.$$

- From $pa + l = ra + n$, we obtain $\dfrac{1}{a}(l - n) = r - p$.

- From $pb + l = qb + m$, we obtain $\dfrac{1}{b}(m - l) = p - q$.

- From $qc + m = rc + n$, we obtain $\dfrac{1}{c}(n - m) = q - r$.

Thus,

$$\frac{1}{b}(m - l) + \frac{1}{a}(l - n) + \frac{1}{c}(n - m)$$
$$= p - q + r - p + q - r$$
$$= 0.$$

Therefore, $\dfrac{1}{b}(m - l) + \dfrac{1}{a}(l - n) + \dfrac{1}{c}(n - m) = 0.$

Problem 124. Let P be the nth degree polynomial such that

$$P(k) = \frac{k - 1}{k + 1}$$

for all $k = \overline{1, n + 1}$. Find $P(n + 3)$.

Solution. Find $P(n + 3)$.

For $k = \overline{1, n + 1}$, we have $P(k) = \dfrac{k - 1}{k + 1}$.

Then $(k + 1) P(k) - (k - 1) = 0$ for all $k = \overline{1, n + 1}$.

Let $Q(x) = (x + 1) P(x) - (x - 1)$. Then $Q(x)$ is a polynomial of degree $n + 1$ with roots $x = 1, 2, ..., n + 1$.

It follows that

$$Q(x) = a(x - 1)(x - 2) \dots (x - n - 1).$$

For $x = -1$, we obtain

$$Q(-1) = a(-1 - 1)(-1 - 2) \dots (-1 - n - 1)$$
$$= a(-2)(-3) \dots (-n - 2)$$

$$= (-1)^{n+1} a (n+2)!.$$

It implies that

$$a = \frac{Q(-1)}{(-1)^{n+1}(n+2)!} = (-1)^{n+1}\frac{Q(-1)}{(n+2)!}.$$

Moreover,

$$Q(-1) = (-1+1)P(-1) - (-1-1) = 2.$$

Then

$$a = (-1)^{n+1}\frac{2}{(n+2)!}.$$

It implies that

$$Q(x) = (-1)^{n+1}\frac{2}{(n+2)!}(x-1)(x-2)\ldots(x-n-1).$$

We obtain

$$Q(n+3) = (-1)^{n+1}\frac{2}{(n+2)!}(n+2)(n+1)\ldots(2)$$

$$= (-1)^{n+1}\frac{2}{(n+2)!}(n+2)!$$

$$= 2(-1)^{n+1}.$$

By knowing that $Q(n+3) = (n+4)P(n+3) - (n+2)$, we obtain

$$(n+4)P(n+3) - (n+2) = 2(-1)^{n+1}.$$

Hence, $P(n+3) = \dfrac{2(-1)^{n+1} + (n+2)}{n+4}.$

$$\boxed{\text{Therefore, } P(n+3) = \frac{2(-1)^{n+1} + (n+2)}{n+4}.}$$

Remark 1. We can more further compute $P(n+3)$ by considering on the parity of n as follows:

- If n is even, then $n+1$ is odd. It follows that $(-1)^{n+1} = -1$. As a result,

$$P(n+3) = \frac{-2+n+2}{n+4} = \frac{n}{n+4}.$$

- If n is odd, then $n+1$ is even. It follows that $(-1)^{n+1} = 1$.
  Hence,
  $$P(n+3) = \frac{2+n+2}{n+4} = \frac{n+4}{n+4} = 1.$$

Problem 125. Given $P(x)$ is a polynomial of degree n such that

$$P(x) = x^n + a_{n-1}x^{n-1} + ... + a_1 x + a_0$$

, where $a_0, a_1, ..., a_{n-1}$ are positive real numbers. Suppose that all roots of $P(x)$ are real numbers. Prove that

$$\frac{\left(n^n + a_{n-1}n^{n-1} + ... + a_1 n + a_0\right)^{n+1}}{(n+1)^{n(n+1)}} \geq a_0.$$

Solution. Prove that $\dfrac{\left(n^n + a_{n-1}n^{n-1} + ... + a_1 n + a_0\right)^{n+1}}{(n+1)^{n(n+1)}} \geq a_0$.

Since $P(x) = x^n + a_{n-1}x^{n-1} + ... + a_1 x + a_0$, where $a_0, a_1, ..., a_{n-1}$ are all positive numbers and its root are all real numbers, from Descartes' rule of signs , we obtain all roots $x_1, x_2, ..., x_n$ of $P(x)$ are negative numbers.

We have $P(x) = (x - x_1)(x - x_2)...(x - x_n)$.

Then $P(n) = (n - x_1)(n - x_2)...(n - x_n)$.

For $i = \overline{1, n}$, from AM-GM inequality, we obtain

$$n - x_i = \underbrace{1 + 1 + ... + 1}_{n} + (-x_i)$$

$$\geq (n+1) \sqrt[n+1]{\underbrace{1 \times 1 \times ... \times 1}_{n}(-x_i)}$$

$$= (n+1) \sqrt[n+1]{-x_i}.$$

It follows that

$$P(n) \geq \left[(n+1) \sqrt[n+1]{-x_1}\right]\left[(n+1) \sqrt[n+1]{-x_2}\right] ... \left[(n+1) \sqrt[n+1]{-x_n}\right]$$

$$= (n+1)^n \sqrt[n+1]{(-1)^n x_1 x_2 ... x_n}.$$

From Vieta's theorem, we obtain $x_1 x_2 ... x_n = (-1)^n \dfrac{a_0}{1} = (-1)^n a_0$.

It follows that

$$P(n) \geq (n+1)^n \sqrt[n+1]{(-1)^n (-1)^n a_0}$$

$$= (n+1)^n \sqrt[n+1]{a_0}.$$

Then $n^n + a_{n-1}n^{n-1} + \ldots + a_1 n + a_0 \geq (n+1)^n \sqrt[n+1]{a_0}.$

Therefore, $\dfrac{\left(n^n + a_{n-1}n^{n-1} + \ldots + a_1 n + a_0\right)^{n+1}}{(n+1)^{n(n+1)}} \geq a_0.$

Problem 126. 1. Given that x_1, x_2 and x_3 are the three roots of $ax^3 + bx^2 + cx + d = 0, a \neq 0$. Let $S_n = x_1^n + x_2^n + x_3^n$ for all $n \geq 0$. Prove that

$$aS_{n+3} + bS_{n+2} + cS_{n+1} + dS_n = 0.$$

2. Given a, b and c are three real numbers such that $a + b + c = 1, a^2 + b^2 + c^2 = 3$ and $a^3 + b^3 + c^3 = 5$. Compute $a^4 + b^4 + c^4$.

Solution. 1. Compute $a^4 + b^4 + c^4$.

Since x_1, x_2 and x_3 are the three roots of the cubic roots $ax^3 + bx^2 + cx + d = 0$, it implies that $ax_1^3 + bx_1^2 + cx_1 + d = 0$. Multiply the above equation by x_1^n, we obtain

$$x_1^n \left(ax_1^3 + bx_1^2 + cx_1 + d\right) = 0.$$

Then $ax_1^{n+3} + bx_1^{n+2} + cx_1^{n+1} + dx_1^n = 0.$
Similarly,

$$ax_2^{n+3} + bx_2^{n+2} + cx_2^{n+1} + dx_2^n = 0$$

and

$$ax_3^{n+3} + bx_3^{n+2} + cx_3^{n+1} + dx_3^n = 0$$

As a result, $a(x_1^{n+3} + x_2^{n+3} + x_3^{n+3}) + b(x_1^{n+2} + x_2^{n+2} + x_3^{n+2}) + c(x_1^{n+1} + x_2^{n+1} + x_3^{n+1}) + d(x_1^n + x_2^n + x_3^n) = 0$

Thus, $aS_{n+3} + bS_{n+2} + cS_{n+1} + dS_n = 0.$

2. Compute $a^4 + b^4 + c^4$.

We know that $(a + b + c)^2 = a^2 + b^2 + c^2 + 2(ab + bc + ca)$.
By knowing that $a + b + c = 1$ and $a^2 + b^2 + c^2 = 3$, we obtain

$$1^2 = 3 + 2(ab + bc + ca).$$

Hence,

$$2(ab + bc + ca) = 1 - 3 = -2.$$

47

It turns out that

$$ab + bc + ca = -1.$$

We have

$$(a + b + c)^3 = a^3 + b^3 + c^3 + 3(a + b)(b + c)(c + a).$$

Since $a + b + c = 1$, then $a + b = 1 - c, b + c = 1 - a$ and $c + a = 1 - b$.
It implies that

$$1^3 = 5 + 3(1 - a)(1 - b)(1 - c)..$$

Then

$$1 = 5 + 3\left[1 - (a + b + c) + (ab + bc + ca) - abc\right].$$

We obtain $-\dfrac{4}{3} = 1 - 1 - 1 - abc.$

Hence, $abc = \dfrac{4}{3} - 1 = \dfrac{1}{3}.$

It turns out that a, b and c are the three roots of the cubic equation $X^3 - X^2 - X - \dfrac{1}{3} = 0.$

From (1), we have

$$S_{n+3} - S_{n+2} - S_{n+1} - \frac{1}{3}S_n = 0.$$

Then

$$S_{n+3} = S_{n+2} + S_{n+1} + \frac{1}{3}S_n.$$

It follows that

$$S_4 = S_3 + S_2 + \frac{1}{3}S_1$$

$$= 5 + 3 + \frac{1}{3}\,(1)$$

$$= 8 + \frac{1}{3}$$

$$= \frac{24 + 1}{3}$$

$$= \frac{25}{3}.$$

Therefore, $a^4 + b^4 + c^4 = \dfrac{25}{3}.$

Problem 127. Suppose that x_1, x_2 and x_3 are the three roots of the cubic equation $x^3 - x^2 + x - 2021 = 0$. Compute

$$S = \frac{(x_1 + x_2)(x_2 + x_3)(x_3 + x_1)}{(1 + x_1)(1 + x_2)(1 + x_3)}.$$

Solution. Compute S

To compute S, we use the following identity:

$$(x - a)(x - b)(x - c) = x^3 - (a + b + c)x^2 + (ab + bc + ca)x - abc$$

Since x_1, x_2 and x_3 are the three roots of the cubic equation $x^3 - x^2 + x - 2021 = 0$, from Vieta's theorem, it implies that

$$\begin{cases} x_1 + x_2 + x_3 = -\dfrac{b}{a} = 1 \\ x_1 x_2 + x_2 x_3 + x_3 x_1 = \dfrac{c}{a} = 1 \\ x_1 x_2 x_3 = -\dfrac{d}{a} = 2021 \end{cases}.$$

From $x_1 + x_2 + x_3 = 1$, we obtain $\begin{cases} x_1 + x_2 = 1 - x_3 \\ x_2 + x_3 = 1 - x_1 \\ x_3 + x_1 = 1 - x_2 \end{cases}.$

Hence,

$$\begin{aligned} S &= \frac{(1 - x_3)(1 - x_1)(1 - x_2)}{(1 + x_1)(1 + x_2)(1 + x_3)} \\ &= \frac{1^3 - (x_1 + x_2 + x_3) \times 1^2 + (x_1 x_2 + x_2 x_3 + x_3 x_1) \times 1 - x_1 x_2 x_3}{1^3 + (x_1 + x_2 + x_3) \times 1^2 + (x_1 x_2 + x_2 x_3 + x_3 x_1) \times 1 + x_1 x_2 x_3} \\ &= \frac{1 - (x_1 + x_2 + x_3) + (x_1 x_2 + x_2 x_3 + x_3 x_1) - x_1 x_2 x_3}{1 + (x_1 + x_2 + x_3) + (x_1 x_2 + x_2 x_3 + x_3 x_1) + x_1 x_2 x_3} \\ &= \frac{1 - 1 + 1 - 2021}{1 + 1 + 1 + 2021} \\ &= \frac{-2020}{2024} \\ &= -\frac{505}{506}. \end{aligned}$$

Therefore, $S = -\dfrac{505}{506}.$

Problem 128. Let a, b and c be the three roots of the cubic equation $P(x) = x^3 - k_1 x^2 + k_2 x - k_3$. Assume that $Q(x) =$

$x^3 + l_1 x^2 + l_2 x + l_3$ has three roots which are $bc - a^2, ca - b^2$ and $ab - c^2$. Prove that

$$\left(k_2^6 + k_2^4 + k_2^2 + 1\right)\left(l_3^2 + l_2^2 + l_1^2 + 1\right) - k_1^2 k_3^2 \geq 0.$$

Solution. Prove that

$$\left(k_2^6 + k_2^4 + k_2^2 + 1\right)\left(l_3^2 + l_2^2 + l_1^2 + 1\right) - k_1^2 k_3^2 \geq 0.$$

Since a, b, c are the three roots of the cubic equation $P(x) = x^3 -$

$k_1 x^2 + k_2 x - k_3$, using Vieta's theorem, we obtain $\begin{cases} a + b + c = k_1 \\ ab + bc + ca = k_2 \\ abc = k_3 \end{cases}$.

We know that $Q(x)$ is a third degree polynomial with leading coefficient x^3 quals 1. Moreover, $bc - a^2, ca - b^2$ and $ab - c^2$ are the three roots of $Q(x)$. Then

$$Q\left(x\right) = \left[x - \left(bc - a^2\right)\right]\left[x - \left(ca - b^2\right)\right]\left[x - \left(ab - c^2\right)\right]$$
$$= \left(x - bc + a^2\right)\left(x - ca + b^2\right)\left(x - ab + c^2\right).$$

Then $Q\left(k_2\right) = \left(k_2 - bc + a^2\right)\left(k_2 - ca + b^2\right)\left(k_2 - ab + c^2\right)$.
Since $ab + bc + ca = k_2$, we obtain

$$Q\left(k_2\right) = \left(ab + bc + ca - bc + a^2\right)\left(ab + bc + ca - ca + b^2\right)$$
$$\times \left(ab + bc + ca - ab + c^2\right)$$
$$= \left(ab + ca + a^2\right)\left(ab + bc + b^2\right)\left(bc + ca + c^2\right)$$
$$= a\left(a + b + c\right)b\left(a + b + c\right)c\left(a + b + c\right)$$
$$= abc\left(a + b + c\right).$$

From $a + b + c = k_1$ and $abc = k_3$, it follows that $Q\left(k_2\right) = k_3 k_1$.
Furthermore, $Q\left(k_2\right) = k_2^3 + l_1 k_2^2 + l_2 k_2 + l_3$.
Using Cauchy-Schwarz inequality, it follows that

$$Q\left(k_2\right) \leq \sqrt{\left(k_2^6 + k_2^4 + k_2^2 + 1\right)\left(1 + l_1^2 + l_2^2 + l_3^2\right)}.$$

Then $k_1 k_3 \leq \sqrt{\left(k_2^6 + k_2^4 + k_2^2 + 1\right)\left(1 + l_1^2 + l_2^2 + l_3^2\right)}$.

$\boxed{\text{Therefore, } \left(k_2^6 + k_2^4 + k_2^2 + 1\right)\left(l_3^2 + l_2^2 + l_1^2 + 1\right) - k_1^2 k_3^2 \geq 0.}$

Problem 129. Compute

$$S = \frac{1}{\cos x \cos 2x} + \frac{1}{\cos 2x \cos 3x} + \ldots + \frac{1}{\cos(n-1)x \cos nx}$$

for all $n \geq 2$.

Solution. Compute S.
We have $\sin x = \sin(2x - x) = \sin 2x \cos x - \sin x \cos 2x$.
Then

$$\begin{aligned}
\frac{\sin x}{\cos x \cos 2x} &= \frac{\sin 2x \cos x - \sin x \cos 2x}{\cos x \cos 2x} \\
&= \frac{\sin 2x}{\cos 2x} - \frac{\sin x}{\cos x} \\
&= \tan 2x - \tan x.
\end{aligned}$$

We obtain $\dfrac{1}{\cos x \cos 2x} = \dfrac{1}{\sin x}(\tan 2x - \tan x)$.
Similarly,

$$\frac{1}{\cos 2x \cos 3x} = \frac{1}{\sin x}(\tan 3x - \tan 2x),$$

$$\vdots$$

and $\quad \dfrac{1}{\cos(n-1)x \cos nx} = \dfrac{1}{\sin x}(\tan nx - \tan(n-1)x).$

Adding all of the above equalities, it implies that

$$S = \frac{1}{\sin x}(\tan nx - \tan x).$$

Therefore, $S = \dfrac{1}{\sin x}(\tan nx - \tan x).$

Problem 130. Suppose that a, b and c are three real numbers such that $a^2 + b^3 + c^4 = 1$. Prove that $a^3 + b^3 + c^3 \leq \sqrt{a^4 + b^3 + c^2}$.

Solution. Prove that $a^3 + b^3 + c^3 \leq \sqrt{a^4 + b^3 + c^2}$.
Since $a^2 + b^3 + c^4 = 1$, it follows that

$$a^4 + b^3 + c^2$$

51

$$= \left(a^4 + b^3 + c^2\right)(1)$$
$$= \left(a^4 + b^3 + c^2\right)\left(a^2 + b^3 + c^4\right)$$
$$= a^6 + a^4 b^3 + a^4 c^4 + a^2 b^3 + b^6 + b^3 c^4 + a^2 c^2 + b^3 c^2 + c^6$$
$$= a^6 + b^6 + c^6 + \left(a^4 b^3 + a^2 b^3\right) + \left(a^4 c^4 + a^2 c^2\right) + \left(b^3 c^4 + b^3 c^2\right)$$
$$= a^6 + b^6 + c^6 + a^2 b^3 \left(a^2 + 1\right) + a^2 c^2 \left(a^2 c^2 + 1\right) + b^3 c^2 \left(c^2 + 1\right).$$

Using AM-GM inequality, we obtain $a^2 + 1 \geq 2\sqrt{a^2 \times 1} = 2a$, $a^2 c^2 + 1 \geq 2\sqrt{a^2 c^2 \times 1} = 2ac$ and $c^2 + 1 \geq 2\sqrt{c^2 \times 1} = 2c$. Then

$$a^4 + b^3 + c^2 \geq a^6 + b^6 + c^6 + a^2 b^3 \left(2a\right) + a^2 c^2 \left(2ac\right) + b^3 c^2 \left(2c\right)$$
$$= a^6 + b^6 + c^6 + 2a^3 b^3 + 2a^3 c^3 + 2b^3 c^3$$
$$= \left(a^3\right)^2 + \left(b^3\right)^2 + \left(c^3\right)^2 + 2a^3 b^3 + 2a^3 c^3 + 2b^3 c^3$$
$$= \left(a^3 + b^3 + c^3\right)^2.$$

Therefore, $a^3 + b^3 + c^3 \leq \sqrt{a^4 + b^3 + c^2}.$

Problem 131. Given the Fibonacci sequence $\{f_n\}$ which is defined by $f_0 = 0, f_1 = 1$ and $f_n = f_{n-1} + f_{n-2}$ for all $n \geq 2$. Prove the following equalities:

1. $f_1 + f_2 + f_3 + ... + f_n = f_{n+2} + 1$ for all $n \geq 1$;

2. $f_1 f_4 + f_2 f_5 + f_3 f_6 + ... + f_{n-2} f_{n+1} = f_n^2 - 1$ for all $n \geq 2$;

3. $f_1^2 + f_2^2 + ... + f_n^2 = f_n f_{n+1}$ for all $n \geq 1$;

4. $f_{n-1} f_{n+1} - f_n^2 = (-1)^n$; for all $n \geq 2$ (Cassini's identity);

5. $x^n = f_n x + f_{n-1}$ for all $n \geq 2$ and x such that $x^2 = x + 1$;

6. $f_n = \dfrac{1}{\sqrt{5}}\left[\left(\dfrac{1+\sqrt{5}}{2}\right)^n - \left(\dfrac{1-\sqrt{5}}{2}\right)^n\right]$ (Binet's Formula).

Solution. Prove the following equalities:

1. $f_1 + f_2 + f_3 + ... + f_n = f_{n+2} + 1$ for all $n \geq 1$
   By definition, we have $f_n = f_{n-1} + f_{n-2}$ for all $n \geq 2$.
   Then $f_{n-2} = f_n - f_{n-1}$.
   Hence,

$$f_1 = f_3 - f_2;$$

$$f_2 = f_4 - f_3;$$
$$f_3 = f_5 - f_4;$$
$$\vdots$$
$$\text{and} \quad f_n = f_{n+2} - f_{n+1}.$$

Adding all of the above equalities, we obtain

$$f_1 + f_2 + \dots + f_n = f_{n+2} - f_2 = f_{n+2} - 1.$$

$$\boxed{\text{Therefore, } f_1 + f_2 + \dots + f_n = f_{n+2} - 1.}$$

2. $f_1 f_4 + f_2 f_5 + f_3 f_6 + \dots + f_{n-2} f_{n+1} = f_n^2 - 1$ for all $n \geq 2$
Fro all positive integers $k \geq 2$, we have

$$f_{k-2} f_{k+1} = (f_k - f_{k-1})(f_k + f_{k-1})$$
$$= f_k^2 - f_{k-1}^2.$$

For $k = 3, 4, \dots,$ and n, we obtain

$$f_1 f_4 = f_3^2 - f_2^2;$$
$$f_2 f_5 = f_4^2 - f_3^2;$$
$$f_3 f_6 = f_5^2 - f_4^2;$$
$$\vdots$$
$$\text{and} \quad f_{n-2} f_{n+1} = f_n^2 - f_{n-1}^2.$$

Adding all of the above equalities, we obtain

$$f_1 f_4 + f_2 f_5 + f_3 f_6 + \dots + f_{n-2} f_{n+1} = f_n^2 - f_2^2 = f_n^2 - 1.$$

$$\boxed{\text{Therefore, } f_1 f_4 + f_2 f_5 + f_3 f_6 + \dots + f_{n-2} f_{n+1} = f_n^2 - 1.}$$

3. $f_1^2 + f_2^2 + \dots + f_n^2 = f_n f_{n+1}$ for all $n \geq 1$
We have

$$f_{n-1} f_{n+1} = (f_{n+1} - f_n)(f_n + f_{n-1})$$
$$= f_{n+1} f_n - f_n^2 + f_{n+1} f_{n-1} - f_n f_{n-1}.$$

Then $f_n^2 = f_{n+1} f_n - f_n f_{n-1}.$
It follows that

$$f_1^2 = f_2 f_1 - f_1 f_0;$$

53

$$f_2^2 = f_3 f_2 - f_2 f_1;$$
$$f_3^2 = f_4 f_3 - f_3 f_2;$$
$$\vdots$$
$$\text{and} \quad f_n^2 = f_{n+1} f_n - f_n f_{n-1}.$$

Adding all of the above equalities, we obtain

$$f_1^2 + f_2^2 + \dots + f_n^2 = f_n f_{n+1} - f_0 = f_n f_{n+1}.$$

$$\boxed{\text{Therefore, } f_1^2 + f_2^2 + \dots + f_n^2 = f_n f_{n+1}.}$$

4. $f_{n-1} f_{n+1} - f_n^2 = (-1)^n$ for all $n \geq 2$
   We have

$$\begin{aligned}
f_{n-1} f_{n+1} - f_n^2 &= (f_n - f_{n-2})(f_n + f_{n-1}) - f_n^2 \\
&= f_n^2 + f_n f_{n-1} - f_{n-2} f_n - f_{n-2} f_{n-1} - f_n^2 \\
&= -f_{n-2} f_n + f_{n-1}(f_n - f_{n-2}) \\
&= -f_{n-2} f_n + f_{n-1}^2 \\
&= -(f_{n-2} f_n - f_{n-1}^2).
\end{aligned}$$

Let $v_n = f_{n-1} f_{n+1} - f_n^2$. Then $v_n = -v_{n-1}$. It follows that $\{v_n\}$ is a geometric sequence such that $v_1 = f_0 f_2 - f_1^2 = -1$ and the common ratio $q = -1$. It implies that

$$v_n = v_1 q^{n-1} = (-1)(-1)^{n-1} = (-1)^n..$$

$$\boxed{\text{Therefore, } f_{n-1} f_{n+1} - f_n^2 = (-1)^n.}$$

5. $x^n = f_n x + f_{n-1}$ for all $n \geq 2$
   We will show the given identity by using induction on n.
   For $n = 2$, we obtain $x^n = f_n x + f_{n-1}$. Then $x^2 = f_2 x + f_1 = x^2 + 1$, true. Suppose that the given identity is true for n. That is, $x^n = f_n x + f_{n-1}$. Next, we will show that the identity is true for $n + 1$. That is, $x^{n+1} = f_{n+1} x + f_n$. We have

$$\begin{aligned}
x^{n+1} = x^n x &= (f_n x + f_{n-1})x \\
&= f_n x^2 + f_{n-1} x = f_n(x + 1) + f_{n-1} x \\
&= x(f_n + f_{n-1}) + f_n
\end{aligned}$$

$$= x f_{n+1} + f_n.$$

Therefore, $x^n = f_n x + f_{n-1}.$

6. $f_n = \dfrac{1}{\sqrt{5}} \left[\left(\dfrac{1 + \sqrt{5}}{2} \right)^n - \left(\dfrac{1 - \sqrt{5}}{2} \right)^n \right]$

The equation $x^2 = x + 1$ has two distinct roots

$$x = \frac{1 + \sqrt{5}}{2}$$

and

$$1 - x = \frac{1 - \sqrt{5}}{2}.$$

From the above proof,

$$x^n = x f_n + f_{n-1}$$

and

$$(1 - x)^n = (1 - x) f_n + f_{n-1}.$$

It follows that $x^n - (1 - x)^n = \sqrt{5} f_n.$

Therefore, $f_n = \dfrac{1}{\sqrt{5}} \left[\left(\dfrac{1 + \sqrt{5}}{2} \right)^n - \left(\dfrac{1 - \sqrt{5}}{2} \right)^n \right].$

Problem 132. Given the Fibonacci sequence $\{f_n\}$. Compute

$$S = \frac{f_1}{f_2^2 + f_1 f_2} + \frac{f_2}{f_3^2 + f_2 f_3} + \dots + \frac{f_n}{f_{n+1}^2 + f_{n+1} f_n}.$$

Solution. Compute S.
For all $k \geq 1$, we obtain

$$\frac{f_k}{f_{k+1}^2 + f_{k+1} f_k} = \frac{f_k}{f_{k+1}(f_{k+1} + f_k)}$$

$$= \frac{f_{k+2} - f_{k+1}}{f_{k+1} f_{k+2}}$$

$$= \frac{f_{k+2}}{f_{k+1} f_{k+2}} - \frac{f_{k+1}}{f_{k+1} f_{k+2}}$$

$$= \frac{1}{f_{k+1}} - \frac{1}{f_{k+2}}.$$

55

It follows that

$$\frac{f_1}{f_2^2 + f_1 f_2} = \frac{1}{f_2} - \frac{1}{f_3};$$

$$\frac{f_2}{f_3^2 + f_2 f_3} = \frac{1}{f_3} - \frac{1}{f_4};$$

$$\frac{f_3}{f_4^2 + f_3 f_4} = \frac{1}{f_4} - \frac{1}{f_5};$$

$$\vdots$$

and $\quad \dfrac{f_n}{f_{n+1}^2 + f_{n+1} f_n} = \dfrac{1}{f_{n+1}} - \dfrac{1}{f_{n+2}}.$

Adding all of the above equalities, we obtain

$$S = \frac{1}{f_2} - \frac{1}{f_{n+2}}$$

$$= \frac{1}{1} - \frac{1}{f_{n+2}}$$

$$= 1 - \frac{1}{f_{n+2}}.$$

Therefore, $S = 1 - \dfrac{1}{f_{n+2}}.$

Problem 133. Given the Fibonacci sequence $\{f_n\}$. Prove that

$$C(n,1) f_1 + C(n,2) f_2 + \ldots + C(n,n) f_n = f_{2n}.$$

Solution. Prove that

$$C(n,1) f_1 + C(n,2) f_2 + \ldots + C(n,n) f_n = f_{2n}.$$

From Binet's Formula, we have

$$f_n = \frac{1}{\sqrt{5}} \left[\left(\frac{1 + \sqrt{5}}{2} \right)^n - \left(\frac{1 - \sqrt{5}}{2} \right)^n \right]$$

for all $n \geq 0$. Let $x_1 = \dfrac{1 + \sqrt{5}}{2}$ and $x_2 = \dfrac{1 - \sqrt{5}}{2}$.
We obtain $f_n = \dfrac{1}{\sqrt{5}} (x_1^n - x_2^n)$ for all $n \geq 0$.

It follows that

$$f_0 = \frac{1}{\sqrt{5}} \left(x_1^0 - x_2^0 \right);$$

$$f_1 = \frac{1}{\sqrt{5}} \left(x_1^1 - x_2^1 \right);$$

$$f_2 = \frac{1}{\sqrt{5}} \left(x_1^2 - x_2^2 \right);$$

$$\vdots$$

$$\text{and} \quad f_n = \frac{1}{\sqrt{5}} \left(x_1^n - x_2^n \right).$$

Hence,

$$C(n,1) f_1 + C(n,2) f_2 + \dots + C(n,n) f_n$$
$$= C(n,0) f_0 + C(n,1) f_1 + C(n,2) f_2 + \dots + C(n,n) f_n$$
$$= \frac{1}{\sqrt{5}} \left[C(n,0) x_1^0 + C(n,1) x_1^1 + \dots + C(n,n) x_1^n \right]$$
$$- \frac{1}{\sqrt{5}} \left[C(n,0) x_2^0 + C(n,1) x_2^1 + \dots + C(n,n) x_2^n \right]$$
$$= \frac{1}{\sqrt{5}} (1 + x_1)^n - \frac{1}{\sqrt{5}} (1 + x_2)^n$$
$$= \frac{1}{\sqrt{5}} \left[(1 + x_1)^n - (1 + x_2)^n \right].$$

Since

$$1 + x_1 = 1 + \frac{1 + \sqrt{5}}{2}$$
$$= \frac{2 + 1 + \sqrt{5}}{2}$$
$$= \frac{3 + \sqrt{5}}{2}$$
$$= \frac{6 + 2\sqrt{5}}{4}$$
$$= \frac{\sqrt{5^2} + 2\sqrt{5} + 1^2}{2^2}$$
$$= \frac{\left(\sqrt{5} + 1 \right)^2}{2^2}$$

$$= \left(\frac{\sqrt{5}+1}{2} \right)^2,$$

it follows that $1 + x_1 = x_1^2$. Then $(1 + x_1)^n = \left(x_1^2 \right)^n = x_1^{2n}$.
Similarly, $(1 + x_2)^n = \left(x_2^2 \right)^n = x_2^{2n}$. We obtain

$$C\left(n,1\right) f_1 + C\left(n,2\right) f_2 + \ldots + C\left(n,n\right) f_n$$

$$= \frac{1}{\sqrt{5}} \left(x_1^{2n} - x_2^{2n} \right)$$

$$= f_{2n}.$$

Therefore, $C\left(n,1\right) f_1 + C\left(n,2\right) f_2 + \ldots + C\left(n,n\right) f_n = f_{2n}.$

Problem 134.   1. Compute $\displaystyle\lim_{n \to +\infty} \frac{1^k + 2^k + \ldots + n^k}{n^{k+1}}$.

2. For all real numbers $x > -1$, prove that

$$\frac{x}{l + (l-1)\,x} \leq \sqrt[l]{1+x} - 1 \leq \frac{x}{l}$$

, where $l \geq 2$.

3. Compute $\displaystyle\lim_{n \to +\infty} \left(-n + \sum_{k=1}^{n} \sqrt[l]{1 + \frac{k^{l-1}}{n^l}} \right)$ for all $l \geq 2$.

Solution.   1. Compute $\displaystyle\lim_{n \to +\infty} \frac{1^k + 2^k + \ldots + n^k}{n^{k+1}}$.
     We have

$$\lim_{n \to +\infty} \frac{1^k + 2^k + \ldots + n^k}{n^{k+1}}$$

$$= \lim_{n \to +\infty} \frac{1}{n} \left[\left(\frac{1}{n} \right)^k + \left(\frac{2}{n} \right)^k + \ldots + \left(\frac{n}{n} \right)^k \right]$$

$$= \lim_{n \to +\infty} \frac{1}{n} \sum_{i=1}^{n} \frac{1}{n} \left(\frac{i}{n} \right)^k$$

$$= \lim_{n \to +\infty} \frac{1}{n} \sum_{i=1}^{n} \Delta x f\left(x_i\right)$$

, where $\Delta x = \dfrac{b-a}{n} = \dfrac{1}{n}$ and $f(x_i) = \left(\dfrac{i}{n}\right)^k$.

For $\dfrac{b-a}{n} = \dfrac{1}{n}$, we obtain $b = a+1$.

Taking $a = 0$, we obtain $b = 0 + 1 = 1$.

Since $x_i = x_0 + i\Delta x = a + i\dfrac{b-a}{n} = 0 + \dfrac{i}{n} = \dfrac{i}{n}$, it follows that $f(x_i) = x_i^k$. Then $f(x) = x^k$.

By definition of definite integral, we obtain

$$\lim_{n \to +\infty} \frac{1^k + 2^k + ... + n^k}{n^{k+1}} = \int_0^1 f(x)dx$$

$$= \int_0^1 x^k dx$$

$$= \left[\frac{x^{k+1}}{k+1}\right]_0^1$$

$$= \frac{1^{k+1}}{k+1} - \frac{0^{k+1}}{k+1}$$

$$= \frac{1}{k+1}.$$

Therefore, $\lim\limits_{n \to +\infty} \dfrac{1^k + 2^k + ... + n^k}{n^{k+1}} = \dfrac{1}{k+1}$.

2. Prove that $\dfrac{x}{l + (l-1)x} \le \sqrt[l]{1+x} - 1 \le \dfrac{x}{l}$.

We have

$$\frac{x}{l + (l-1)x} + 1 = \frac{x + l + lx - x}{l + lx - x}$$

$$= \frac{l(1+x)}{1 + (l-1)(1+x)}$$

$$= \frac{l}{\dfrac{1 + (l-1)(1+x)}{1+x}}$$

$$= \frac{l}{\dfrac{1}{1+x} + l - 1}$$

59

$$= \frac{l}{\frac{1}{1+x} + \underbrace{1+1+\ldots+1}_{l-1}}.$$

Using AM-GM-HM inequality, we obtain

$$\frac{x}{l + (l-1)\,x} + 1 \leq \sqrt[l]{(1+x)\left(\underbrace{1 \times 1 \times \ldots \times 1}_{l-1}\right)}$$

$$\leq \frac{1 + x + \underbrace{1+1+\ldots+1}_{l-1}}{l}$$

$$\frac{x}{l + (l-1)\,x} + 1 \leq \sqrt[l]{1+x} \leq \frac{1 + x + l - 1}{l}$$

$$\frac{x}{l + (l-1)\,x} + 1 \leq \sqrt[l]{1+x} \leq \frac{x}{l} + 1$$

$$\frac{x}{l + (l-1)\,x} \leq \sqrt[l]{1+x} - 1 \leq \frac{x}{l}.$$

Therefore, $\dfrac{x}{l + (l-1)\,x} \leq \sqrt[l]{1+x} - 1 \leq \dfrac{x}{l}.$

3. Compute $\displaystyle\lim_{n \to +\infty} \left(-n + \sum_{k=1}^{n} \sqrt[l]{1 + \frac{k^{l-1}}{n^l}} \right).$

We have

$$\lim_{n \to +\infty} \left(-n + \sum_{k=1}^{n} \sqrt[l]{1 + \frac{k^{l-1}}{n^l}} \right) = \lim_{n \to +\infty} \left(\sum_{k=1}^{n} \sqrt[l]{1 + \frac{k^{l-1}}{n^l}} - 1 \right).$$

From (2), we obtain

$$\frac{x}{l + (l-1)\,x} \leq \sqrt[l]{1+x} - 1 \leq \frac{x}{l}.$$

Let $x = \dfrac{k^{l-1}}{n^l}$. We obtain

$$\frac{\dfrac{k^{l-1}}{n^l}}{l + (l-1)\left(\dfrac{k^{l-1}}{n^l}\right)} \leq \sqrt[l]{1 + \frac{k^{l-1}}{n^l}} - 1 \leq \frac{\dfrac{k^{l-1}}{n^l}}{l}$$

60

$$\frac{k^{l-1}}{n^l l + k^{l-1}(l-1)} \le \sqrt[l]{1 + \frac{k^{l-1}}{n^l}} - 1 \le \frac{k^{l-1}}{n^l l}$$

$$\sum_{k=1}^{n} \frac{k^{l-1}}{n^l l + k^{l-1}(l-1)} \le \sum_{k=1}^{n} \left(\sqrt[l]{1 + \frac{k^{l-1}}{n^l}} - 1 \right) \le \sum_{k=1}^{n} \frac{k^{l-1}}{n^l l}.$$

$$(1)$$

We have

$$\lim_{n \to +\infty} \sum_{k=1}^{n} \frac{k^{l-1}}{n^l l} = \lim_{n \to +\infty} \frac{1}{l} \sum_{k=1}^{n} \frac{k^{l-1}}{n^l}$$

$$= \frac{1}{l}\left(\frac{1}{l}\right)$$

$$= \frac{1}{l^2}.$$

Moreover,

$$\lim_{n \to +\infty} \sum_{k=1}^{n} \frac{k^{l-1}}{n^l l + k^{l-1}(l-1)} \ge \lim_{n \to +\infty} \sum_{k=1}^{n} \frac{k^{l-1}}{n^l l + n^{l-1}(l-1)}.$$

From (1), we obtain $\sum_{k=1}^{n} k^{l-1}$ is a polynomial of degree l in n.

Moreover, the coefficient of n^l in $P(x)$ is equal to $\frac{1}{l}$. Hence,

$$\lim_{n \to +\infty} \sum_{k=1}^{n} \frac{k^{l-1}}{n^l l + n^{l-1}(l-1)} = \frac{1}{l^2}.$$

Then $\lim_{n \to +\infty} \sum_{k=1}^{n} \frac{k^{l-1}}{n^l l + k^{l-1}(l-1)} \ge \frac{1}{l^2}$.

Using Sandwich theorem and (1), we obtain

$$\lim_{n \to +\infty} \left(-n + \sum_{k=1}^{n} \sqrt[l]{1 + \frac{k^{l-1}}{n^l}} \right) = \frac{1}{l^2}.$$

Therefore, $\lim_{n \to +\infty} \left(-n + \sum_{k=1}^{n} \sqrt[l]{1 + \frac{k^{l-1}}{n^l}} \right) = \frac{1}{l^2}.$

Problem 135. Given a real sequence $\{a_n\}$ such that $a_1 = 1$ and $a_{n+1}^3 = a_n^3 + 3n^2 + 3n + 1$ for all positive integer n.

1. Find the nth term of $\{a_n\}$;

2. Compute $\displaystyle\sum_{k=1}^{n} \frac{1}{a_k \left(a_k + 1\right)\left(a_k + 2\right)}$.

Solution.   1. Find the nth term of $\{a_n\}$.
We know that $a_1 = 1$ and $a_{n+1}^3 = a_n^3 + 3n^2 + 3n + 1$ for all $n \geq 1$.
Then

$$a_{n+1}^3 - a_n^3 = 3n^2 + 3n + 1.$$

It follows that

$$a_2^3 - a_1^3 = 3\left(1^2\right) + 3\left(1\right) + 1;$$
$$a_3^3 - a_2^3 = 3\left(2^2\right) + 3\left(2\right) + 1;$$
$$a_4^3 - a_3^3 = 3\left(3^2\right) + 3\left(3\right) + 1;$$

$$\vdots$$

$$\text{and} \quad a_n^3 - a_{n-1}^3 = 3(n-1)^2 + 3\left(n-1\right) + 1.$$

Adding all of the above equalities, we obtain

$$
\begin{aligned}
a_n^3 - a_1^3 &= 3\sum_{k=1}^{n-1} k^2 + 3\sum_{k=1}^{n-1} k + \sum_{k=1}^{n-1} 1 \\
&= \frac{3n\left(n-1\right)\left(2n-1\right)}{6} + \frac{3n\left(n-1\right)}{2} + \left(n-1\right) \\
&= \frac{\left(n-1\right)\left[n\left(2n-1\right) + 3n + 2\right]}{2} \\
&= \frac{\left(n-1\right)\left(2n^2 + 2n + 2\right)}{2} \\
&= \left(n-1\right)\left(n^2 + n + 1\right) \\
&= n^3 - 1.
\end{aligned}
$$

Then $a_n^3 - 1 = n^3 - 1$. Hence, $a_n = n$.

$\boxed{\text{Therefore, } a_n = n \text{ for all } n \geq 1.}$

2. Compute $\displaystyle\sum_{k=1}^{n} \frac{1}{a_k\,(a_k+1)\,(a_k+2)}$.

Since $a_n = n$, we obtain

$$\sum_{k=1}^{n} \frac{1}{a_k\,(a_k+1)\,(a_k+2)} = \sum_{k=1}^{n} \frac{1}{k\,(k+1)\,(k+2)}$$

$$= \sum_{k=1}^{n} \frac{1}{2}\left[\frac{1}{k\,(k+1)} - \frac{1}{(k+1)\,(k+2)}\right]$$

$$= \frac{1}{2}\sum_{k=1}^{n}\left[\frac{1}{k\,(k+1)} - \frac{1}{(k+1)\,(k+2)}\right]$$

$$= \frac{1}{2}\left[\frac{1}{1\times 2} - \frac{1}{(n+1)\,(n+2)}\right]$$

$$= \frac{1}{2}\left[\frac{1}{2} - \frac{1}{(n+1)\,(n+2)}\right]$$

$$= \frac{(n+1)\,(n+2) - 2}{4\,(n+1)\,(n+2)}$$

$$= \frac{n^2 + 3n + 2 - 2}{4\,(n+1)\,(n+2)}$$

$$= \frac{n\,(n+3)}{4\,(n+1)\,(n+2)}.$$

Therefore, $\displaystyle\sum_{k=1}^{n} \frac{1}{a_k\,(a_k+1)\,(a_k+2)} = \frac{n\,(n+3)}{4\,(n+1)\,(n+2)}.$

Problem 136. Let P_n be the product of the first n terms of the sequence $\{a_n\}$. Suppose that $P_n = n!$ for all positive integers n.

1. Find the nth term of $\{a_n\}$.

2. Let $S_n = a_1^4 + a_2^4 + a_3^4 + \ldots + a_n^4$. Find S_n in terms of n.

Solution. 1. Find the nth term of $\{a_n\}$.

We have $P_n = n!$. Then $P_{n-1} = (n-1)!$ for all $n \geq 2$.

Then

$$\frac{P_n}{P_{n-1}} = \frac{n!}{(n-1)!} = \frac{n \times (n-1)!}{(n-1)!} = n.$$

By knowing that $\dfrac{P_n}{P_{n-1}} = a_n$, we obtain $a_n = n$ for all $n \geq 2$.

For $n = 1$, we obtain $a_1 = P_1 = 1$.

$$\boxed{\text{Therefore, } a_n = n \text{ for all } n \geq 1.}$$

2. Find S_n in terms of n.

Since $a_n = n$, we obtain $S_n = a_1^4 + a_2^4 + a_3^4 + \ldots + a_n^4$

$$= 1^4 + 2^4 + 3^4 + \ldots + n^4.$$

For all positive integers k, we obtain

$$(k+1)^5 = k^5 + 5k^4 + 10k^3 + 10k^2 + 5k + 1.$$

Then $(k+1)^5 - k^5 = 5k^4 + 10k^3 + 10k^2 + 5k + 1$.

It follows

$$2^5 - 1^5 = 5\left(1^4\right) + 10\left(1^3\right) + 10\left(1^2\right) + 5\left(1\right) + 1;$$
$$3^5 - 2^5 = 5\left(2^4\right) + 10\left(2^3\right) + 10\left(2^2\right) + 5\left(2\right) + 1;$$
$$4^5 - 3^5 = 5\left(3^4\right) + 10\left(3^3\right) + 10\left(3^2\right) + 5\left(3\right) + 1;$$

$$\vdots$$

and $\quad (n+1)^5 - n^5 = 5\left(n^4\right) + 10\left(n^3\right) + 10\left(n^2\right) + 5\left(n\right) + 1.$

Adding all of the above equalities, we obtain

$$(n+1)^5 - 1 = 5S_n + 10\sum_{k=1}^{n}k^3 + 10\sum_{k=1}^{n}k^2 + 5\sum_{k=1}^{n}k + n.$$

Then

$$5S_n = (n+1)^5 - (n+1) - 10\sum_{k=1}^{n}k^3 - 10\sum_{k=1}^{n}k^2 - 5\sum_{k=1}^{n}k$$

$$= (n+1)^5 - (n+1) - \frac{10n^2(n+1)^2}{4} - \frac{10n\left(n+1\right)\left(2n+1\right)}{6}$$
$$- \frac{5n\left(n+1\right)}{2}$$

$$= (n+1)^5 - (n+1) - \frac{5n^2(n+1)^2}{2} - \frac{10n\left(n+1\right)\left(2n+1\right)}{6}$$
$$- \frac{5n\left(n+1\right)}{2}$$

$$= \frac{(n+1)\left[6(n+1)^4 - 6 - 5n^2\left(n+1\right) - 10n\left(2n+1\right) - 5n\right]}{6}$$

$$= \frac{n(n+1)\left(6n^3 + 9n^2 + n - 1\right)}{6}$$

$$= \frac{n(n+1)(2n+1)\left(3n^2 + 3n - 1\right)}{6}.$$

Therefore, $S_n = \dfrac{n(n+1)(2n+1)\left(3n^2 + 3n - 1\right)}{30}.$

Problem 137. Given a real sequence $\{u_n\}$ which is defined by

$$u_n = \frac{1}{\sqrt{1}} + \frac{1}{\sqrt{2}} + \dots + \frac{1}{\sqrt{n}} - 2\sqrt{n} + 2$$

for all positive integers $n \geq 1$. Prove that $\{u_n\}$ is a convergent sequence.

Solution. Prove that $\{u_n\}$ is a convergent sequence.

We have $u_n = \dfrac{1}{\sqrt{1}} + \dfrac{1}{\sqrt{2}} + \dots + \dfrac{1}{\sqrt{n}} - 2\sqrt{n} + 2.$

Then $u_{n+1} = \dfrac{1}{\sqrt{1}} + \dfrac{1}{\sqrt{2}} + \dots + \dfrac{1}{\sqrt{n+1}} - 2\sqrt{n+1} + 2.$

It follows that

$$u_{n+1} = u_n + 2\sqrt{n} - 2 + \frac{1}{\sqrt{n+1}} - 2\sqrt{n+1} + 2$$

$$= u_n + \frac{1}{\sqrt{n+1}} + 2\left(\sqrt{n} - \sqrt{n+1}\right)$$

$$= u_n + \frac{1}{\sqrt{n+1}} + 2\left(\frac{\sqrt{n}^2 - \sqrt{n+1}^2}{\sqrt{n} + \sqrt{n+1}}\right)$$

$$= u_n + \frac{1}{\sqrt{n+1}} + 2\left(\frac{n - n - 1}{\sqrt{n} + \sqrt{n+1}}\right)$$

$$= u_n + \frac{1}{\sqrt{n+1}} - \frac{2}{\sqrt{n+1} + \sqrt{n}}$$

$$= u_n + \frac{\sqrt{n+1} + \sqrt{n} - 2\sqrt{n+1}}{\sqrt{n+1}\left(\sqrt{n+1} + \sqrt{n}\right)}$$

$$= u_n + \frac{\sqrt{n} - \sqrt{n+1}}{\sqrt{n+1}\left(\sqrt{n+1} + \sqrt{n}\right)}.$$

Then

$$u_{n+1} - u_n = \frac{\sqrt{n} - \sqrt{n+1}}{\sqrt{n+1}\left(\sqrt{n+1} + \sqrt{n}\right)} < 0$$

65

for all $n \geq 1$.

Then $\{u_n\}$ is a decreasing sequence.

For all positive integers k, we have

$$\frac{1}{2\sqrt{k}} = \frac{1}{\sqrt{k} + \sqrt{k}}$$

$$> \frac{1}{\sqrt{k+1} + \sqrt{k}}$$

$$> \frac{\sqrt{k+1} - \sqrt{k}}{\left(\sqrt{k+1} + \sqrt{k}\right)\left(\sqrt{k+1} - \sqrt{k}\right)}$$

$$= \frac{\sqrt{k+1} - \sqrt{k}}{\sqrt{(k+1)^2} - \sqrt{k^2}}$$

$$= \frac{\sqrt{k+1} - \sqrt{k}}{k+1 - k}$$

$$= \sqrt{k+1} - \sqrt{k}.$$

Then $\dfrac{1}{\sqrt{k}} > 2\left(\sqrt{k+1} - \sqrt{k}\right)$.

Taking $k = 1, 2, 3, ...,$ and n, we obtain

$$\frac{1}{\sqrt{1}} > 2\left(\sqrt{2} - \sqrt{1}\right);$$

$$\frac{1}{\sqrt{2}} > 2\left(\sqrt{3} - \sqrt{2}\right);$$

$$\frac{1}{\sqrt{3}} > 2\left(\sqrt{4} - \sqrt{3}\right);$$

$$\vdots$$

$$\text{and} \quad \frac{1}{\sqrt{n}} > 2\left(\sqrt{n+1} - \sqrt{n}\right).$$

Adding all of the above inequality, we obtain

$$\frac{1}{\sqrt{1}} + \frac{1}{\sqrt{2}} + ... + \frac{1}{\sqrt{n}} > 2\left(\sqrt{n+1} - 1\right)$$

for all $n \geq 1$.

It implies that

$$u_n > 2\left(\sqrt{n+1} - 1\right) - 2\sqrt{n} + 2$$

$$= 2\sqrt{n+1} - 2 - 2\sqrt{n} + 2$$
$$= 2\sqrt{n+1} - 2\sqrt{n}$$
$$= 2\left(\sqrt{n+1} - \sqrt{n}\right) > 0$$

for all $n \geq 1$.

Then $\{u_n\}$ is bounded below.

From Monotone Convergence Theorem, we obtain $\{u_n\}$ converges.

Therefore, $\{u_n\}$ is convergent.

Problem 138. Without using the calculator, prove that

$$\frac{\sin 22° \sin 40°}{\sin 33° \sin 44°} < \frac{20}{33} \left(\frac{\cos 22° \cos 40°}{\cos 33° \cos 44°} \right).$$

Solution. Prove that $\dfrac{\sin 22° \sin 40°}{\sin 33° \sin 44°} < \dfrac{20}{33} \left(\dfrac{\cos 22° \cos 40°}{\cos 33° \cos 44°} \right).$

The above inequality is equivalent to

$$33 \tan 22° \tan 40° < 20 \tan 33° \tan 44°.$$

Hence, to prove the above inequality, it is sufficient to prove that

$$33 \tan 22° \tan 40° < 20 \tan 33° \tan 44°.$$

Let f be a function which is defined by $f(x) = \dfrac{\tan x}{x}$. We have

$$f'(x) = \left(\frac{\tan x}{x} \right)'$$
$$= \frac{(\tan x)' x - (x)' \tan x}{x^2}$$
$$= \frac{\left(\dfrac{1}{\cos^2 x} \right) x - \tan x}{x^2}$$
$$= \frac{\dfrac{x}{\cos^2 x} - \dfrac{\sin x}{\cos x}}{x^2}$$
$$= \frac{\dfrac{x - \sin x \cos x}{\cos^2 x}}{x^2}$$
$$= \frac{x - \sin x \cos x}{x^2 \cos^2 x}$$

67

$$= \frac{2x - 2\sin x \cos x}{2x^2 \cos^2 x}$$

$$= \frac{2x - \sin 2x}{2x^2 \cos^2 x}.$$

Since $x > \sin x$ for all $x > 0$, we obtain $2x > \sin 2x$ for all $x > 0$. Then $f'(x) > 0$ for all $x > 0$. That is, f is an increasing function on $(0, +\infty)$.

- Since $\dfrac{22\pi}{180} < \dfrac{33\pi}{180}$, we obtain

$$\frac{\tan \dfrac{22\pi}{180}}{\dfrac{22\pi}{180}} < \frac{\tan \dfrac{33\pi}{180}}{\dfrac{33\pi}{180}}$$

$$\frac{\tan 22°}{22} < \frac{\tan 33°}{33}$$

$$3\tan 22° < 2\tan 33°.$$

- Since $\dfrac{40}{180}\pi < \dfrac{44}{180}\pi$, we obtain

$$\frac{\tan \dfrac{40}{180}\pi}{\dfrac{40}{180}\pi} < \frac{\tan \dfrac{44}{180}\pi}{\dfrac{44}{180}\pi}$$

$$\frac{\tan 40°}{40} < \frac{\tan 44°}{44}$$

$$11\tan 40° < 10\tan 44°.$$

From $3\tan 22° < 2\tan 33°$ and $11\tan 40° < 10\tan 44°$, we obtain

$$(3\tan 22°)(11\tan 40°) < (2\tan 33°)(10\tan 44°).$$

It implies that $33\tan 22° \tan 40° < 20\tan 33° \tan 44°$.

$\boxed{\text{Therefore, the given inequality is proved.}}$

Problem 139. For all $p \geq 2$, prove that the real sequence $\{u_n\}$ which is defined by $u_n = \dfrac{1}{1^p} + \dfrac{1}{2^p} + \dfrac{1}{3^p} + ... + \dfrac{1}{n^p}$ is a convergent sequence.

Solution. Prove that $\{u_n\}$ is a convergent sequence.
For all $n \geq 2$, it follows that

$$
\begin{aligned}
u_n &= \frac{1}{1^p} + \frac{1}{2^p} + \frac{1}{3^p} + \dots + \frac{1}{n^p} \\
&< 1 + \frac{1}{1 \times 2} + \frac{1}{2 \times 3} + \dots + \frac{1}{(n-1)\,n} \\
&= 1 + \left(1 - \frac{1}{2}\right) + \left(\frac{1}{2} - \frac{1}{3}\right) + \dots + \left(\frac{1}{n-1} - \frac{1}{n}\right) \\
&= 1 - \frac{1}{n} \\
&< 1.
\end{aligned}
$$

Moreover, $u_1 = 1$. Then $u_n \leq 1$ for all $n \geq 1$.
It follows that $\{u_n\}$ is bounded above.
Furthermore,

$$
\begin{aligned}
u_{n+1} &= \frac{1}{1^p} + \frac{1}{2^p} + \frac{1}{3^p} + \dots + \frac{1}{n^p} + \frac{1}{(n+1)^p} \\
&> \frac{1}{1^p} + \frac{1}{2^p} + \frac{1}{3^p} + \dots + \frac{1}{n^p} \\
&= u_n
\end{aligned}
$$

for all $n \geq 1$.
It follows that $\{u_n\}$ is an increasing sequence. From Monotone
Convergence Theorem, we obtain $\{u_n\}$ converges.

Therefore, $\{u_n\}$ is convergent.

Problem 140. Given a real sequence $\{u_n\}$ which is defined by
$u_1 = \sqrt[k]{a}$ and $u_{n+1} = \sqrt[k]{a + \sqrt[k]{u_n}}$, where $a > 2$. Prove that $\{u_n\}$
is convergent.

Solution. Prove that $\{u_n\}$ is convergent.
We have $u_1 = \sqrt[k]{a}$ and $u_{n+1} = \sqrt[k]{a + \sqrt[k]{u_n}}$.
Then $u_2 = \sqrt[k]{a + \sqrt[k]{u_1}} = \sqrt[k]{a + \sqrt[k]{a}} > \sqrt[k]{a} = u_1$.
Suppose that $u_{n+1} > u_n$. We will show that $u_{n+2} > u_{n+1}$.
From the induction hypothesis, we have $u_{n+1} > u_n$. It follows that

$$
\sqrt[k]{u_{n+1}} > \sqrt[k]{u_n}.
$$

Then $a + \sqrt[k]{u_{n+1}} > a + \sqrt[k]{u_n}$.
It follows that

$$\sqrt[k]{a + \sqrt[k]{u_{n+1}}} > \sqrt[k]{a + \sqrt[k]{u_n}}.$$

Hence, $u_{n+2} > u_{n+1}$.
From induction, it implies that $u_{n+1} > u_n$ for all $n \geq 1$.
It follows that $\{u_n\}$ is increasing. To prove that $\{u_n\}$ is convergent, it is sufficient to prove that $\{u_n\}$ is bounded above.
We have $u_1 = \sqrt[k]{a} < a$ because $a > 2$.
Suppose that $u_n < a$. We shall show that $u_{n+1} < a$.
Since $u_n < a$, we obtain

$$\begin{aligned} u_{n+1} &= \sqrt[k]{a + \sqrt[k]{u_n}} \\ &< \sqrt[k]{a + \sqrt[k]{a}} \\ &< \sqrt[k]{a + a} \\ &= \sqrt[k]{2a} < a. \end{aligned}$$

Consequently, $u_n < a$ for all $n \geq 1$. It follows that $\{u_n\}$ is bounded above.

Therefore, $\{u_n\}$ is convergent.

Problem 141. Given a real sequence $\{u_n\}$ which is defined by $u_n = \dfrac{n}{a^n}$ for all $n \geq 1$ and $a \geq 2$. Prove that $\{u_n\}$ is convergent and find its limit.

Solution. Prove that $\{u_n\}$ is convergent and find its limit.
We have $u_n = \dfrac{n}{a^n}$. Then $u_{n+1} = \dfrac{n+1}{a^{n+1}}$. It follows that

$$\begin{aligned} \frac{u_{n+1}}{u_n} &= \frac{\dfrac{n+1}{a^{n+1}}}{\dfrac{n}{a^n}} \\ &= \frac{n+1}{a^{n+1}} \times \frac{a^n}{n} \\ &= \frac{n+1}{an}. \end{aligned}$$

Since $a \geq 2$, it follows that $an \geq 2n \geq n + 1$. Then $\dfrac{u_{n+1}}{u_n} \leq 1$. It is obvious to see that all terms of $\{u_n\}$ are positive. Then $u_{n+1} \leq$

u_n for all $n \geq 1$. It follows that $\{u_n\}$ is decreasing. Hence, to prove that $\{u_n\}$ is convergent, it is sufficient to prove that $\{u_n\}$ is bounded below. It is trivial to see that $u_n > 0$ for all $n \geq 1$. Then $\{u_n\}$ is bounded below. From Monotone Convergence Theorem, we obtain $\{u_n\}$ is convergent.

Therefore, $\{u_n\}$ is convergent.

By knowing that $\{u_n\}$ is convergent, then it has a unique limit. Let l be the limit of $\{u_n\}$. From $u_{n+1} = \dfrac{n+1}{an} u_n$, we obtain $l = \dfrac{1}{a} l$. Solve the last equation, we obtain $l = 0$.

$$\boxed{\text{Therefore, } \lim_{n \to +\infty} u_n = 0.}$$

Problem 142. For all positive integers n, prove that

$$\frac{1}{2n+1} < \frac{1}{2} \times \frac{3}{4} \times \ldots \times \frac{2n-1}{2n} < \frac{1}{\sqrt{2n+1}}.$$

Solution. Prove that $\dfrac{1}{2n+1} < \dfrac{1}{2} \times \dfrac{3}{4} \times \ldots \times \dfrac{2n-1}{2n} < \dfrac{1}{\sqrt{2n+1}}$.

For all positive real numbers a and b such that $a < b$, we obtain

$$\frac{1}{a} > \frac{1}{b}.$$

For all positive integers k, we obtain $2k < 2k+1$. Then

$$\frac{1}{2k} > \frac{1}{2k+1}.$$

It follows that $\dfrac{2k-1}{2k} > \dfrac{2k-1}{2k+1}$.

Taking $k = 1, 2, 3, \ldots$ and n, we obtain

$$\frac{1}{2} > \frac{1}{3};$$
$$\frac{3}{4} > \frac{3}{5};$$
$$\vdots$$

$$\text{and} \quad \frac{2n-1}{2n} > \frac{2n-1}{2n+1}.$$

Multiply all of the above inequalities, we obtain

$$\frac{1}{2} \times \frac{3}{4} \times \ldots \times \frac{2n-1}{2n} > \frac{1}{3} \times \frac{3}{5} \times \frac{5}{7} \times \ldots \times \frac{2n-1}{2n+1}.$$

71

Then

$$\frac{1}{2} \times \frac{3}{4} \times ... \times \frac{2n-1}{2n} > \frac{1}{2n+1}. \qquad (1)$$

Moreover, for all positive integers k, we have

$$(k-1)(k+1) = k^2 - 1 < k^2.$$

Then $\dfrac{k-1}{k} < \dfrac{k}{k+1}.$

Taking $k = 2, 4, ...,$ and $2n$, we obtain

$$\frac{1}{2} < \frac{2}{3};$$

$$\frac{3}{4} < \frac{4}{5};$$

$$\vdots$$

$$\text{and} \quad \frac{2n-1}{2n} < \frac{2n}{2n+1};$$

Multiply all of the above inequalities, we obtain

$$\frac{1}{2} \times \frac{3}{4} \times ... \times \frac{2n-1}{2n} < \frac{2}{3} \times \frac{4}{5} \times ... \times \frac{2n}{2n+1}$$

$$= \frac{2}{1} \times \frac{4}{3} \times ... \times \frac{2n}{2n-1} \times \frac{1}{2n+1}.$$

It follows that $\left(\dfrac{1}{2} \times \dfrac{3}{4} \times ... \times \dfrac{2n-1}{2n}\right)^2 < \dfrac{1}{2n+1}.$

Then

$$\frac{1}{2} \times \frac{3}{4} \times ... \times \frac{2n-1}{2n} < \sqrt{\frac{1}{2n+1}}. \qquad (2)$$

From (1) and (2), we obtain

$$\frac{1}{2n+1} < \frac{1}{2} \times \frac{3}{4} \times ... \times \frac{2n-1}{2n} < \frac{1}{\sqrt{2n+1}}.$$

Therefore, $\dfrac{1}{2n+1} < \dfrac{1}{2} \times \dfrac{3}{4} \times ... \times \dfrac{2n-1}{2n} < \dfrac{1}{\sqrt{2n+1}}.$

Problem 143. For all positive integers $n > 1$, prove that

$$n\left(\sqrt[n]{n+1} - 1 - \frac{1}{n+1}\right) < 1 + \frac{1}{2} + \frac{1}{3} + ... + \frac{1}{n} - \frac{n}{n+1}$$

$$< n\left(1 - \frac{1}{\sqrt[n]{n+1}}\right).$$

Solution. Prove that

$$n\left(\sqrt[n]{n+1} - 1 - \frac{1}{n+1}\right) < 1 + \frac{1}{2} + \frac{1}{3} + \ldots + \frac{1}{n} - \frac{n}{n+1}$$

$$< n\left(1 - \frac{1}{\sqrt[n]{n+1}}\right).$$

Using AM-GM inequality, we obtain

$$\frac{2}{1} + \frac{3}{2} + \frac{4}{3} + \ldots + \frac{n+1}{n} > n\sqrt[n]{\left(\frac{2}{1}\right)\left(\frac{3}{2}\right)\left(\frac{4}{3}\right)\ldots\left(\frac{n+1}{n}\right)}$$

$$= n\sqrt[n]{n+1}.$$

Then $(1+1) + \left(1 + \frac{1}{2}\right) + \ldots + \left(1 + \frac{1}{n}\right) > n\sqrt[n]{n+1}.$

It follows that $n + 1 + \frac{1}{2} + \frac{1}{3} + \ldots + \frac{1}{n} > n\sqrt[n]{n+1}.$

Hence,

$$1 + \frac{1}{2} + \frac{1}{3} + \ldots + \frac{1}{n} - \frac{n}{n+1} > n\sqrt[n]{n+1} - n - \frac{n}{n+1}$$

$$= n\left(\sqrt[n]{n+1} - 1 - \frac{1}{n+1}\right). \quad (1)$$

From AM-GM inequality, we have

$$\frac{1}{2} + \frac{2}{3} + \frac{3}{4} + \ldots + \frac{n}{n+1} > n\sqrt[n]{\left(\frac{1}{2}\right)\left(\frac{2}{3}\right)\left(\frac{3}{4}\right)\ldots\left(\frac{n}{n+1}\right)}$$

$$= n\sqrt[n]{\frac{1}{n+1}}$$

$$= \frac{n}{\sqrt[n]{n+1}}.$$

It follows that

$$\left(1 - \frac{1}{2}\right) + \left(1 - \frac{1}{3}\right) + \ldots + \left(1 - \frac{1}{n}\right) + \frac{n}{n+1} > \frac{n}{\sqrt[n]{n+1}}.$$

Then $n - \left(1 + \frac{1}{2} + \frac{1}{3} + \ldots + \frac{1}{n}\right) + \frac{n}{n+1} > \frac{n}{\sqrt[n]{n+1}}.$

It implies that

$$1 + \frac{1}{2} + \frac{1}{3} + \ldots + \frac{1}{n} - \frac{n}{n+1} < n - \frac{n}{\sqrt[n]{n+1}}$$

$$= n \left(1 - \frac{1}{\sqrt[n]{n+1}} \right). \qquad (2)$$

From (1) and (2), we obtain

$$n \left(\sqrt[n]{n+1} - 1 - \frac{1}{n+1} \right)$$
$$< 1 + \frac{1}{2} + \frac{1}{3} + \ldots + \frac{1}{n} - \frac{n}{n+1}$$
$$< n \left(1 - \frac{1}{\sqrt[n]{n+1}} \right)$$

Therefore, $n \left(\sqrt[n]{n+1} - 1 - \dfrac{1}{n+1} \right) < 1 + \dfrac{1}{2} + \dfrac{1}{3} + \ldots + \dfrac{1}{n} - \dfrac{n}{n+1}$

$$< n \left(1 - \frac{1}{\sqrt[n]{n+1}} \right).$$

Problem 144. Prove that $e^x > 1 + x + \dfrac{x^2}{2!} + \ldots + \dfrac{x^n}{n!}$ for all real numbers $x > 0$.

Solution. Prove that $e^x > 1 + x + \dfrac{x^2}{2!} + \ldots + \dfrac{x^n}{n!}$ for all real numbers $x > 0$.

The inequality $e^x > 1 + x + \dfrac{x^2}{2!} + \ldots + \dfrac{x^n}{n!}$ is equivalent to

$$e^x - \left(1 + x + \frac{x^2}{2!} + \ldots + \frac{x^n}{n!} \right) > 0.$$

Let $f(x) = e^x - 1 - x$. We obtain $f'(x) = e^x - 1 > 0$ for all $x > 0$.
Then $e^x - x - 1 > 0$ for all $x > 0$.
Hence, the given inequality holds for $n = 1$.
Suppose that

$$e^x - \left(1 + x + \frac{x^2}{2!} + \ldots + \frac{x^n}{n!} \right) > 0. \qquad (1)$$

We shall show that $e^x - \left[1 + x + \dfrac{x^2}{2} + \ldots + \dfrac{x^{n+1}}{(n+1)!} \right] > 0.$

Let $g(x) = e^x - \left[1 + x + \dfrac{x^2}{2!} + \ldots + \dfrac{x^{n+1}}{(n+1)!} \right].$

Then

$$g'(x) = e^x - \left(1 + x + \frac{x^2}{2} + \dots + \frac{x^n}{n!}\right).$$

From (1), we obtain $g'(x) > 0$.

Hence, g is an increasing function. It implies that $g(x) > g(0)$ for all $x > 0$.

Then $e^x - \left[1 + x + \dfrac{x^2}{2} + \dots + \dfrac{x^{n+1}}{(n+1)!}\right] > 0$.

Therefore, $e^x > 1 + x + \dfrac{x^2}{2!} + \dots + \dfrac{x^n}{n!}$ for all $x > 0$.

Problem 145. Given n is an odd number such that $n \geq 3$. Prove that

$$\left(1 + x + \frac{x^2}{2!} + \frac{x^3}{3!} + \dots + \frac{x^n}{n!}\right)\left(1 - x + \frac{x^2}{2!} - \frac{x^3}{3!} + \dots - \frac{x^n}{n!}\right) \leq 1$$

for all $x \neq 0$.

Solution. Let

$$F(x) = \left(1 + x + \frac{x^2}{2!} + \frac{x^3}{3!} + \dots + \frac{x^n}{n!}\right)$$
$$\times \left(1 - x + \frac{x^2}{2!} - \frac{x^3}{3!} + \dots - \frac{x^n}{n!}\right);$$
$$f(x) = 1 + x + \frac{x^2}{2!} + \frac{x^3}{3!} + \dots + \frac{x^n}{n!};$$
$$\text{and} \quad g(x) = 1 - x + \frac{x^2}{2!} - \frac{x^3}{3!} + \dots - \frac{x^n}{n!}.$$

Then $F(x) = f(x)g(x)$. It follows that

$$F'(x) = f'(x)g(x) + g'(x)f(x).$$

Moreover, $f'(x) = 1 + x + \dfrac{x^2}{2!} + \dots + \dfrac{x^{n-1}}{(n-1)!}$.

It follows that

$$f'(x) = f(x) - \frac{x^n}{n!}.$$

Furthermore,

$$g'(x) = -1 + x - \frac{x^2}{2!} + \dots - \frac{x^{n-1}}{(n-1)!}$$

75

or

$$g'(x) = -g(x) - \frac{x^n}{n!} = -\left[g(x) + \frac{x^n}{n!}\right].$$

It implies that

$$F'(x) = \left[f(x) - \frac{x^n}{n!}\right]g(x) - \left[g(x) + \frac{x^n}{n!}\right]f(x)$$

$$= f(x)g(x) - \frac{x^n}{n!}g(x) - f(x)g(x) - \frac{x^n}{n!}f(x)$$

$$= -\frac{x^n}{n!}[f(x) + g(x)]$$

$$= -\frac{x^n}{n!}\left[2\left(1 + \frac{x^2}{2!} + \frac{x^4}{4!} + ... + \frac{x^{n-1}}{(n-1)!}\right)\right].$$

Hence, $F(x)$ and $-x^n$ have opposite sign. Using the fact that n is an odd number, we obtain $F(x)$ and $-x$ have the same sign.

x	$-\infty$		0		$+\infty$
$F'(x)$		$+$	0	$-$	
$F(x)$	$-\infty$	$\nearrow$	1	$\searrow$	$-\infty$

From the above sign table, we obtain $F(x) \le 1$ for all $x \ne 0$. Therefore,

$$\left(1 + x + \frac{x^2}{2!} + \frac{x^3}{3!} + ... + \frac{x^n}{n!}\right)\left(1 - x + \frac{x^2}{2!} - \frac{x^3}{3!} + ... - \frac{x^n}{n!}\right) \le 1$$

for all $x \ne 0$.

Problem 146. For all positive integers $n \ge 3$, prove that

$$n^{n+1} > (n+1)^n.$$

Solution. Prove that $n^{n+1} > (n+1)^n$.
Method I:

76

For $n = 3$, the given inequality becomes $3^4 > 4^3$ or $81 > 64$, true. Suppose that $n^{n+1} > (n+1)^n$. We shall show that

$$(n+1)^{n+2} > (n+2)^{n+1}.$$

We have

$$n^{n+1} > (n+1)^n$$

or

$$1 > \frac{(n+1)^n}{n^{n+1}}.$$

It follows that

$$(n+1)^{n+2} > \frac{(n+1)^n}{n^{n+1}} \times (n+1)^{n+2}$$

$$= \frac{(n+1)^{2n+2}}{n^{n+1}}$$

$$= \left(\frac{n^2 + 2n + 1}{n}\right)^{n+1}$$

$$= \left(n + 2 + \frac{1}{n}\right)^{n+1} > (n+2)^{n+1}.$$

Therefore, $n^{n+1} > (n+1)^n$ for all $n \geq 3$.

Method II:

Consider on a function f which is defined by $f(x) = \dfrac{x}{\ln x}$ for all $x \geq 3$. We have

$$f'(x) = \frac{(x)' \ln x - (\ln x)' x}{x^2} = \frac{\ln x - 1}{x^2} > 0$$

for all $x \geq 3$.

Then f is an increasing function on $[3, +\infty)$.

For all $n \geq 3$, we obtain

$$\frac{n+1}{\ln(n+1)} > \frac{n}{\ln n}$$

or

$$(n+1) \ln n > n \ln(n+1).$$

Therefore, $n^{n+1} > (n+1)^n$ for all $n \geq 3$.

Problem 147.   1. Prove that $x - \dfrac{x^2}{2} < \ln(1+x) < x$ for all $x > 0$.

2. Given that $S_n = \ln\left[\left(1 + \dfrac{1}{n^2}\right)\left(1 + \dfrac{2}{n^2}\right)\cdots\left(1 + \dfrac{n}{n^2}\right)\right]$.
Compute $\lim\limits_{n \to +\infty} S_n$.

Solution.   1. Prove that $x - \dfrac{x^2}{2} < \ln(1+x) < x$ for all $x > 0$.

Let $f(x) = \ln(1+x) - x + \dfrac{x^2}{2}$, where $x > 0$.

Then $f'(x) = \dfrac{1}{1+x} - 1 + x = \dfrac{x^2}{1+x} > 0$ for all $x > 0$.
It follows that f is an increasing function on $(0, +\infty)$.
Then $f(x) > f(0)$ for all $x > 0$.
It follows that $\ln(1+x) - x + \dfrac{x^2}{2} > \ln 1 - 0 + 0 = 0$. Hence,

$$\ln(1+x) > x - \frac{x^2}{2}. \tag{1}$$

Let $g(x) = x - \ln(1+x)$. It follows that

$$g'(x) = 1 - \frac{1}{1+x} = \frac{x}{1+x} > 0$$

for all $x > 0$. Then g is an increasing function. We obtain
$g(x) > g(0)$ for all $x > 0$.
It implies that

$$x - \ln(1+x) > 0 - \ln 1 = 0$$

or

$$\ln(1+x) < x. \tag{2}$$

From (1) and (2), we obtain

$$x - \frac{x^2}{2} < \ln(1+x) < x$$

for all $x > 0$.

Therefore, $x - \dfrac{x^2}{2} < \ln(1+x) < x$ for all $x > 0$.

2. Compute $\lim\limits_{n \to +\infty} S_n$.

We have $x - \dfrac{x^2}{2} < \ln(1+x) < x$ for all $x > 0$.

Taking $x = \dfrac{k}{n^2}$, we obtain

$$\frac{k}{n^2} - \frac{k^2}{2n^4} < \ln\left(1 + \frac{k}{n^2}\right) < \frac{k}{n^2}.$$

Then $\displaystyle\sum_{k=1}^{n}\left(\frac{k}{n^2} - \frac{k^2}{2n^4}\right) < \sum_{k=1}^{n}\ln\left(1 + \frac{k}{n^2}\right) < \sum_{k=1}^{n}\frac{k}{n^2}.$

It follows that

$$\sum_{k=1}^{n}\left(\frac{k}{n^2} - \frac{k^2}{2n^4}\right) = \left(\frac{1+2+\ldots+n}{n^2}\right) - \frac{1}{2}\left(\frac{1^2 + 2^2 + \ldots + n^2}{n^4}\right)$$

$$= \frac{n(n+1)}{2n^2} - \frac{1}{2}\left[\frac{n(n+1)(2n+1)}{6n^4}\right].$$

Hence, $\displaystyle\lim_{n \to +\infty}\sum_{k=1}^{n}\left(\frac{k}{n^2} - \frac{k^2}{2n^4}\right) = \frac{1}{2}.$

Moreover, $\displaystyle\sum_{k=1}^{n}\left(\frac{k}{n^2}\right) = \frac{n(n+1)}{2n^2}.$ Then

$$\lim_{n \to +\infty}\sum_{k=1}^{n}\left(\frac{k}{n^2}\right) = \frac{1}{2}.$$

Therefore, $\displaystyle\lim_{n \to +\infty} S_n = \frac{1}{2}.$

Problem 148. 1. Prove that

$$\ln(1+x) < x < -\ln(1-x)$$

for all $0 < x < 1$.

2. Given that $S_n = \dfrac{a}{n+a} + \dfrac{a}{n+2a} + \ldots + \dfrac{a}{n+na}$ for all $a > 0$.
Compute $\lim\limits_{n \to +\infty} S_n$.

Solution. 1. Prove that $\ln(1+x) < x < -\ln(1-x)$.
We have $f(x) = x - \ln(1+x)$.

79

Then $f'(x) = 1 - \dfrac{1}{1+x} = \dfrac{x}{x+1} > 0$ for all $0 < x < 1$.

It implies that f is an increasing function on $(0,1)$.

Then $f(x) > f(0)$ for all $0 < x < 1$.

We obtain $x - \ln(1+x) > 0 - \ln 1 = 0$.

Hence,

$$x > \ln(1+x). \tag{1}$$

Let $g(x) = -x - \ln(1-x)$.

Then

$$g'(x) = -1 + \frac{1}{1-x} = \frac{x}{1-x} > 0$$

for all $0 < x < 1$.

Hence, g is an increasing function.

We obtain $g(x) > g(0)$ for all $0 < x < 1$.

Then $-x - \ln(1-x) > 0$.

It follows that

$$x < -\ln(1-x). \tag{2}$$

From (1) and (2), we obtain

$$\ln(1+x) < x < -\ln(1-x)$$

for all $0 < x < 1$.

Therefore, $\ln(1+x) < x < -\ln(1-x)$ for all $0 < x < 1$.

2. Compute $\lim\limits_{n \to +\infty} S_n$.

We have $\ln(1+x) < x < -\ln(1-x)$ for all $0 < x < 1$.

By knowing that $0 < \dfrac{a}{n+ka} < 1$ for all $a > 0$ and $k, n \in \mathbb{N}$,

we obtain

$$\ln\left(1 + \frac{a}{n+ka}\right) < \frac{a}{n+ka} < -\ln\left(1 - \frac{a}{n+ka}\right).$$

It implies that

$$\sum_{k=1}^{n} \ln\left(1 + \frac{a}{n+ka}\right) < S_n < \sum_{k=1}^{n}\left[-\ln\left(1 - \frac{a}{n+ka}\right)\right]$$

$$\sum_{k=1}^{n} \ln\left[\frac{n + (k+1)a}{n+ka}\right] < S_n < -\sum_{k=1}^{n} \ln\left[\frac{n + (k-1)a}{n+ka}\right]$$

$$\ln\left[\frac{n + (n+1)a}{n+a}\right] < S_n < -\ln\left(\frac{n}{n+na}\right)$$

$$\ln \left[\frac{n + (n+1)\, a}{n + a} \right] < S_n < \ln \left(1 + a \right).$$

Then

$$\lim_{n \to +\infty} \ln \left[\frac{n + (n+1)\, a}{n + a} \right] = \lim_{n \to +\infty} \ln \left[\frac{(1+a)\, n + a}{n + a} \right]$$

$$= \ln \left(1 + a \right)$$

and

$$\lim_{n \to +\infty} \ln \left(1 + a \right) = \ln \left(1 + a \right).$$

Hence, $\lim\limits_{n \to +\infty} S_n = \ln(1 + a)$.

$$\boxed{\text{Therefore, } \lim_{n \to +\infty} S_n = \ln(1 + a).}$$

Problem 149. Given M is a point inside triangle ABC. Let x, y and z be the distance from M to the sides $[BC], [CA]$ and $[AB]$ respectively. Find the minimum value of $x^2 + y^2 + z^2$.

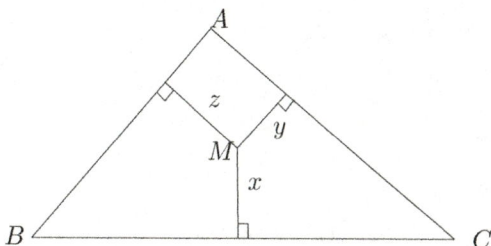

Solution. We have $[BMC] = \dfrac{1}{2} ax$. Then $x = \dfrac{2[BMC]}{a}$.

It follows that $x^2 = \dfrac{4[BMC]^2}{a^2}$.

Similarly, $y^2 = \dfrac{4[AMC]^2}{b^2}$ and $z^2 = \dfrac{4[AMB]^2}{c^2}$.

We thus obtain $x^2 + y^2 + z^2 = 4 \left(\dfrac{[BMC]^2}{a^2} + \dfrac{[AMC]^2}{b^2} + \dfrac{[AMB]^2}{c^2} \right)$.

Using Engel form of Cauchy-Schwarz inequality, we obtain

$$x^2 + y^2 + z^2 \geq \frac{4([BMC] + [AMC] + [AMB])^2}{a^2 + b^2 + c^2}$$

$$= \frac{4S^2}{a^2 + b^2 + c^2}.$$

81

$$\text{Therefore, } \min(x^2 + y^2 + z^2) = \frac{4S^2}{a^2 + b^2 + c^2}.$$

Problem 150.   1. (Van Aubel's Theorem)

Given P is a point inside triangle ABC. $[AP), [BP)$ and $[CP)$ cut sides $[BC], [CA]$ and $[AB]$ at D, E and F respectively. Prove that $\dfrac{AF}{FB} + \dfrac{AE}{EC} = \dfrac{AP}{PD}$.

2. Let I be the center of the inscribed circle of triangle ABC and $[AD)$ is the bisector of $\angle A$. Prove that $\dfrac{AI}{ID} = \dfrac{b+c}{a}$.

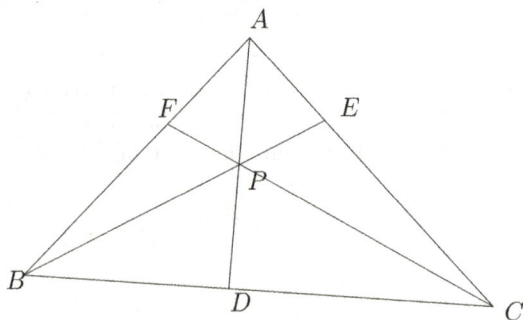

Solution.

1. We have

$$\begin{aligned}
\frac{AF}{BF} &= \frac{[APF]}{[BPF]} \\
&= \frac{[ACF]}{[BCF]} \\
&= \frac{[ACF] - [APF]}{[BCF] - [BPF]} \\
&= \frac{[APC]}{[BPC]}.
\end{aligned}$$

Similarly, $\dfrac{AE}{EC} = \dfrac{[APB]}{[BPC]}$.

Then

$$\frac{AF}{FB} + \frac{AE}{EC} = \frac{[APC]}{[BPC]} + \frac{[APB]}{[BPC]}$$

82

$$= \frac{[APC] + [APB]}{[BPC]}. \tag{1}$$

Moreover,

$$\frac{AP}{PD} = \frac{[APB]}{[BPD]} = \frac{[APC]}{[PCD]}$$
$$= \frac{[APB] + [APC]}{[BPC]}. \tag{2}$$

From (1) and (2), we obtain $\boxed{\dfrac{AF}{FB} + \dfrac{AE}{EC} = \dfrac{AP}{PD}.}$

2. Prove that $\dfrac{AI}{ID} = \dfrac{b+c}{a}.$

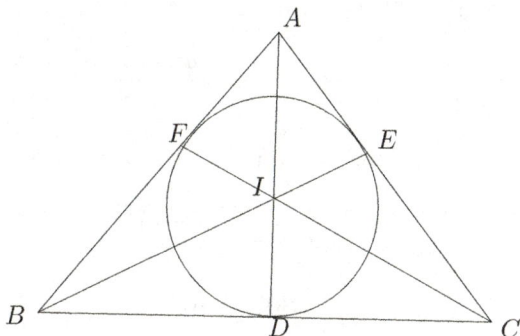

Using Van Aubel's theorem, we obtain

$$\frac{AF}{BE} + \frac{AE}{EC} = \frac{AI}{ID}.$$

Using angle bisector theorem, we have $\dfrac{CA}{AF} = \dfrac{BC}{BF}.$
Then $\dfrac{AF}{FB} = \dfrac{b}{a}.$
Similarly, $\dfrac{AE}{EC} = \dfrac{c}{a}.$ We obtain

$$\frac{AI}{ID} = \frac{b}{a} + \frac{c}{a}$$
$$= \frac{b+c}{a}.$$

83

Therefore, $\dfrac{AI}{ID} = \dfrac{b+c}{a}$.

Problem 151. 1. (Stewart's theorem)

Given a triangle ABC. Let D be a point on the side $[BC]$. Assume that $BC = a, CA = b, AB = c, AD = d, BD = n$ and $CD = m$. Prove that

$$b^2 n + c^2 m = a(d^2 + mn).$$

2. Let m_a be the length of the median of triangle ABC drawing from vertex A. Prove that $m_a^2 = \dfrac{b^2 + c^2}{2} - \dfrac{a^2}{4}$.

3. Given a triangle ABC inscribed in a circle centering at O with radius R. Let G be the centroid of it. Prove that

$$OG^2 = R^2 - \dfrac{a^2 + b^2 + c^2}{9}.$$

4. Let $[AD)$ be the bisector of $\angle A$ of a triangle ABC. Prove that

$$AD = \dfrac{\sqrt{bc\left[(b+c)^2 - a^2\right]}}{b+c}.$$

Solution.

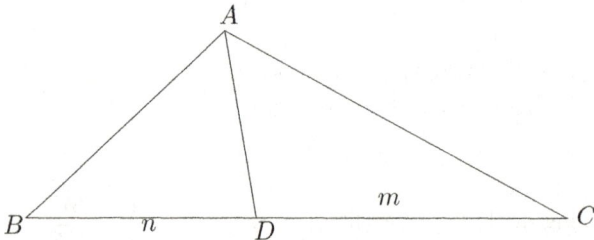

1. Prove that $b^2 n + c^2 m = a(d^2 + mn)$.

Using the law of cosine, we have

$$c^2 = d^2 + n^2 - 2nd \cos \angle ADB.$$

Then

$$c^2 m = d^2 m + mn^2 - 2mnd \cos \angle ADB \qquad \text{(i)}$$

84

and $b^2 = d^2 + m^2 - 2md \cos \angle ADC$.

Since $\angle ADC + \angle ADB = \pi$, it follows that

$$\angle ADC = \pi - \angle ADB.$$

We obtain $\cos \angle ADC = -\cos \angle ADB$.

Then $b^2 = d^2 + m^2 - 2md \cos \angle ADB$.

It implies that

$$b^2 n = d^2 n + m^2 n - 2mnd \cos \angle ADB. \qquad \text{(ii)}$$

Adding (i) and (ii), we obtain

$$\begin{aligned}
c^2 m + b^2 n &= d^2 m + mn^2 + d^2 n + m^2 n \\
&= (m + n)d^2 + mn(m + n) \\
&= ad^2 + amn.
\end{aligned}$$

Therefore, $b^2 n + c^2 m = a(d^2 + mn)$.

2. Prove that $m_a = \dfrac{b^2 + c^2}{2} - \dfrac{a^2}{4}$.

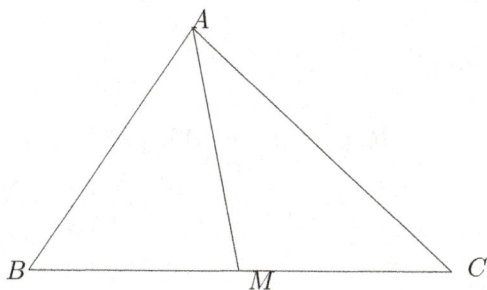

Using Stewart's theorem, we obtain

$$AB^2 \times MC + AC^2 \times BM = BC(AM^2 + BM \times MC)$$

$$c^2 \left(\frac{a}{2}\right) + b^2 \left(\frac{a}{2}\right) = a \left[m_a^2 + \left(\frac{a}{2}\right)\left(\frac{a}{2}\right)\right]$$

$$\frac{b^2 + c^2}{2} = m_a^2 + \frac{a^2}{4}.$$

Therefore, $m_a = \dfrac{b^2 + c^2}{2} - \dfrac{a^2}{4}$.

3. Prove that $OG^2 = R^2 - \dfrac{a^2 + b^2 + c^2}{9}$.

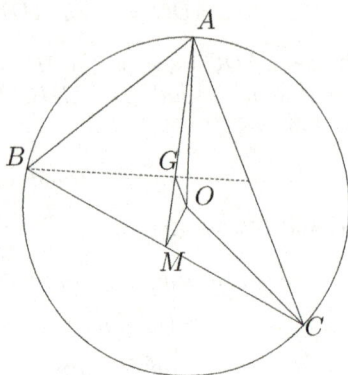

Applying Stewart's theorem in triangle AOM, we obtain

$$OA^2 \times GM + OM^2 \times GA = AM(OG^2 + GA \times GM).$$

By knowing that $GM = \dfrac{1}{3}AM, GA = \dfrac{2}{3}AM, OM^2 = OC^2 -$

$MC^2 = R^2 - \dfrac{a^2}{4}$, we obtain

$$R^2 \left(\frac{1}{3}AM \right) + \frac{2}{3}AM \left(R^2 - \frac{a^2}{4} \right)$$
$$= AM \left[OG^2 + \left(\frac{1}{3}AM \right) \left(\frac{2}{3}AM \right) \right].$$

Then

$$\frac{R^2}{3} + \frac{2}{3} \left(R^2 - \frac{a^2}{4} \right) = OG^2 + \frac{2}{9}AM^2.$$

It implies that

$$R^2 - \frac{a^2}{6} = OG^2 + \frac{2}{9}AM^2.$$

Moreover, $AM^2 = \dfrac{b^2 + c^2}{2} - \dfrac{a^2}{4}$. It follows that

$$R^2 - \frac{a^2}{6} = OG^2 + \frac{2}{9} \left(\frac{b^2 + c^2}{2} - \frac{a^2}{4} \right).$$

Hence,

$$OG^2 = R^2 - \frac{b^2 + c^2}{9} + \frac{a^2}{18} - \frac{a^2}{6}$$

$$= R^2 - \frac{a^2 + b^2 + c^2}{9}.$$

Therefore, $OG^2 = R^2 - \dfrac{a^2 + b^2 + c^2}{9}$.

4. Prove that $AD = \dfrac{\sqrt{bc\left[(b+c)^2 - a^2\right]}}{b+c}$.

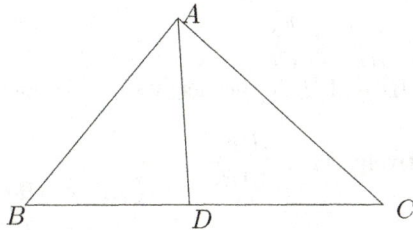

Applying Stewart's theorem, we obtain

$$AB^2 \times CD + AC^2 \times BD = BC(AD^2 + BD \times CD).$$

Since $[AD)$ is the bisector of $\angle A$, it follows that

$$\frac{AB}{BD} = \frac{AC}{CD} = \frac{b+c}{a}.$$

We obtain $BD = \dfrac{ca}{b+c}$ and $CD = \dfrac{ab}{b+c}$.
It implies that

$$\frac{abc^2}{b+c} + \frac{ab^2c}{b+c} = aAD^2 + a\left(\frac{ca}{b+c}\right)\left(\frac{ab}{b+c}\right).$$

Then

$$AD^2 = \frac{bc^2 + b^2c}{b+c} - \frac{a^2bc}{(b+c)^2}$$

$$= \frac{bc(b+c)^2 - a^2bc}{(b+c)^2}$$

87

Therefore, $AD = \dfrac{\sqrt{bc\left[(b+c)^2 - a^2\right]}}{b+c}.$

Problem 152. Let K be a point in triangle ABC. $[AK), [BK)$ and $[CK)$ cut sides $[BC], [CA]$ and $[AB]$ at A_1, B_1 and C_1 respectively. Prove that

1. $\dfrac{KA_1}{AA_1} + \dfrac{KB_1}{BB_1} + \dfrac{KC_1}{CC_1} = 1;$

2. $\dfrac{AK}{AA_1} + \dfrac{BK}{BB_1} + \dfrac{CK}{CC_1} = 2.$

Solution. Prove that

1. $\dfrac{KA_1}{AA_1} + \dfrac{KB_1}{BB_1} + \dfrac{KC_1}{CC_1} = 1$

   Let $[AH]$ and $[KN]$ be heights of triangle ABC and BKC

   respectively. Then $\dfrac{[BKC]}{[ABC]} = \dfrac{\dfrac{1}{2}BC \times KN}{\dfrac{1}{2}BC \times AH} = \dfrac{KN}{AH}.$

   Moreover, $[AH]//[KN]$. It follows that $\dfrac{KN}{AH} = \dfrac{KA_1}{AA_1}.$

   It implies that $\dfrac{[BKC]}{[ABC]} = \dfrac{KA_1}{AA_1}.$

   Similarly, $\dfrac{[AKC]}{[ABC]} = \dfrac{KB_1}{BB_1}$ and $\dfrac{[AKB]}{[ABC]} = \dfrac{KC_1}{CC_1}.$

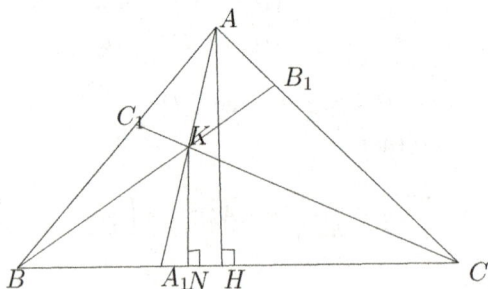

Hence,

$$\dfrac{KA_1}{AA_1} + \dfrac{KB_1}{BB_1} + \dfrac{KC_1}{CC_1} = \dfrac{[BKC] + [AKC] + [AKB]}{[ABC]}$$

$$= \frac{[ABC]}{[ABC]} = 1.$$

Therefore, $\dfrac{KA_1}{AA_1} + \dfrac{KB_1}{BB_1} + \dfrac{KC_1}{CC_1} = 1.$

2. $\dfrac{AK}{AA_1} + \dfrac{BK}{BB_1} + \dfrac{CK}{CC_1} = 2$

We have $\dfrac{KA_1}{AA_1} + \dfrac{KB_1}{BB_1} + \dfrac{KC_1}{CC_1} = 1.$

Then $\dfrac{AA_1 - AK}{AA_1} + \dfrac{BB_1 - BK}{BB_1} + \dfrac{CC_1 - CK}{CC_1} = 1.$

It follows that $1 - \dfrac{AK}{AA_1} + 1 - \dfrac{BK}{BB_1} + 1 - \dfrac{CK}{CC_1} = 1.$

Therefore, $\dfrac{AK}{AA_1} + \dfrac{BK}{BB_1} + \dfrac{CK}{CC_1} = 3 - 1 = 2.$

Problem 153. Given a triangle ABC. Let a, b, c be the lengths of the three sides and h_a, h_b, h_c be the lengths of heights drawing from vertices A, B and C respectively. Let d_a, d_b and d_c be the lengths from the orthocenter of triangle ABC to the vertices A, B and C respectively. Prove that

$$h_a d_a + h_b d_b + h_c d_c = \frac{a^2 + b^2 + c^2}{2}.$$

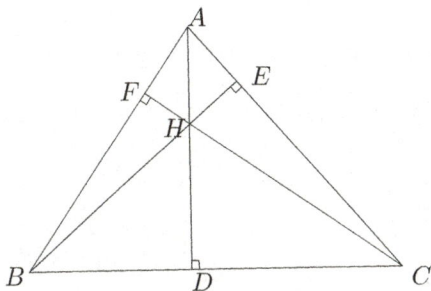

Solution.
Let D, E, F be the points of perpendicular projection of A, B, C on $[BC], [CA], [AB]$ respectively. Assume further H is the orthocenter of triangle ABC. It follows that $\triangle ACD \sim \triangle AHE$.

As a result, $\dfrac{AC}{AH} = \dfrac{AD}{AE} = \dfrac{CD}{HE}$. Then

$$AD \times AH = AE \times AC = b \times AE.$$

It implies that

$$h_a d_a = b \times AE. \tag{1}$$

Similarly, $\triangle ABD \sim \triangle AHF$.

As a result, $\dfrac{AB}{AH} = \dfrac{AD}{AF} = \dfrac{BD}{HF}$. Then

$$AD \times AH = AF \times AB = c \times AF.$$

Consequently,

$$h_a d_a = c \times AF. \tag{2}$$

Adding (1) and (2), we obtain $h_a d_a = \dfrac{AE \times b + AF \times c}{2}$.

Similarly, we obtain

$$h_b d_b = \dfrac{BF \times c + BD \times a}{2}$$

and

$$h_c d_c = \dfrac{CD \times a + CE \times b}{2}.$$

It follows that

$$h_a d_a + h_b d_b + h_c d_c$$
$$= \dfrac{a^2 + b^2 + c^2}{2}$$
$$= \dfrac{1}{2}(AE \times b + AF \times c + BF \times c + BD \times a + CD \times a + CE \times b)$$
$$= \dfrac{1}{2}[(BD + CD)a + (CE + AE)b + (AF + BF)c]$$
$$= \dfrac{a^2 + b^2 + c^2}{2}.$$

Therefore, $h_a d_a + h_b d_b + h_c d_c = \dfrac{a^2 + b^2 + c^2}{2}$.

Problem 154. Given r and R are the radii of the inscribed circle and the circumscribed circle of triangle ABC. Prove that

$$a + b + c \geq 2\sqrt{3r(r + 4R)}.$$

Solution. Prove that $a + b + c \geq 2\sqrt{3r(r + 4R)}$.

We have

$$(a + b + c)^2 \geq 3(ab + bc + ca) \tag{1}$$

Using area formula, we have

$$S = pr = \sqrt{p(p - a)(p - b)(p - c)}.$$

Squaring both sides of the last equality, we obtain

$$(pr)^2 = p(p - a)(p - b)(p - c).$$

Divide both sides of the above equality by p, it folows that

$$
\begin{aligned}
pr^2 &= (p - a)(p - b)(p - c) \\
&= p^3 - (a + b + c)p^2 + (ab + bc + ca)p - abc \\
&= p^3 - 2p\left(p^2\right) + (ab + bc + ca)\,p - 4R\left(\frac{abc}{4R}\right) \\
&= p^3 - 2p^3 + (ab + bc + ca)\,p - 4R\,(pr) \\
&= -p^3 + (ab + bc + ca)\,p - 4prR \\
&= p\left(-p^2 + ab + bc + ca - 4rR\right).
\end{aligned}
$$

As a result,

$$r^2 = -p^2 + ab + bc + ca - 4rR.$$

Then

$$ab + bc + ca = p^2 + r^2 + 4rR.$$

From (1), it implies that

$$(a + b + c)^2 \geq 3(p^2 + r^2 + 4rR).$$

Then

$$(2p)^2 \geq 3\left(p^2 + r^2 + 4rR\right).$$

It turns out that

$$4p^2 \geq 3p^2 + 3r(r + 4R).$$

Hence,

$$p^2 \geq 3r(r + 4R).$$

We obtain $p \geq \sqrt{3r(r + 4R)}$.

Therefore, $a + b + c \geq 2\sqrt{3r(r + 4R)}$.

Problem 155. Given r and R are the radii of the inscribed circle and the circumscribed circle of triangle ABC. Prove that

$$\frac{1}{\sin\dfrac{A}{2}} + \frac{1}{\sin\dfrac{B}{2}} + \frac{1}{\sin\dfrac{C}{2}} \geq 4\sqrt{\frac{R}{r}}.$$

Solution. Prove that $\dfrac{1}{\sin\dfrac{A}{2}} + \dfrac{1}{\sin\dfrac{B}{2}} + \dfrac{1}{\sin\dfrac{C}{2}} \geq 4\sqrt{\dfrac{R}{r}}$.

Observe that

$$\begin{aligned}
\sin^2\frac{A}{2} &= \frac{1 - \cos A}{2} \\
&= \frac{1 - \dfrac{b^2 + c^2 - a^2}{2bc}}{2} \\
&= \frac{a^2 - (b^2 - 2bc + c^2)}{4bc} \\
&= \frac{a^2 - (b - c)^2}{4bc} \\
&= \frac{(a - b + c)(a + b - c)}{4bc} \\
&= \frac{(p - b)(p - c)}{bc}.
\end{aligned}$$

Then $\sin\dfrac{A}{2} = \sqrt{\dfrac{(p-b)(p-c)}{bc}}$.

Similarly,

$$\sin\frac{B}{2} = \sqrt{\frac{(p-c)(p-a)}{ca}}$$

and

$$\sin\frac{C}{2} = \sqrt{\frac{(p-a)(p-b)}{ab}}.$$

It follows that

$$\sin\frac{A}{2}\sin\frac{B}{2}\sin\frac{C}{2} = \frac{(p-a)(p-b)(p-c)}{abc}.$$

Since $S = \sqrt{p(p-a)(p-b)(p-c)}$, we obtain

$$(p-a)(p-b)(p-c) = \frac{S^2}{p} = \frac{prS}{p} = rS.$$

Moreover, $\dfrac{abc}{4R} = S$. Then $abc = 4RS$.

It implies that $\sin\dfrac{A}{2}\sin\dfrac{B}{2}\sin\dfrac{C}{2} = \dfrac{rS}{4RS} = \dfrac{r}{4R} = \dfrac{r}{4R}$.

Then $\dfrac{R}{r} = \dfrac{1}{4\sin\frac{A}{2}\sin\frac{B}{2}\sin\frac{C}{2}}$.

Hence, $\dfrac{1}{\sin\frac{A}{2}} + \dfrac{1}{\sin\frac{B}{2}} + \dfrac{1}{\sin\frac{C}{2}} \geq 4\sqrt{\dfrac{R}{r}}$.

The above inequality is equivalent to

$$\frac{1}{\sin\frac{A}{2}} + \frac{1}{\sin\frac{B}{2}} + \frac{1}{\sin\frac{C}{2}} \geq 4\sqrt{\frac{1}{4\frac{1}{\sin\frac{A}{2}}\frac{1}{\sin\frac{B}{2}}\frac{1}{\sin\frac{C}{2}}}}$$

or

$$\sqrt{\frac{\sin\frac{B}{2}\sin\frac{C}{2}}{\sin\frac{A}{2}}} + \sqrt{\frac{\sin\frac{C}{2}\sin\frac{A}{2}}{\sin\frac{B}{2}}} + \sqrt{\frac{\sin\frac{A}{2}\sin\frac{B}{2}}{\sin\frac{C}{2}}} \geq 2 \qquad (1)$$

To prove that the given inequality holds, it is sufficient to prove that (1) is true.

We have

$$\sin\frac{B}{2}\sin\frac{C}{2} = \sqrt{\frac{(p-c)(p-a)}{ca}}\sqrt{\frac{(p-a)(p-b)}{ab}}$$

$$= \left(\frac{p-a}{a}\right)\sqrt{\frac{(p-b)(p-c)}{bc}}$$

$$= \left(\frac{p-a}{a}\right)\sin\frac{A}{2}.$$

Hence, $\dfrac{\sin\frac{B}{2}\sin\frac{C}{2}}{\sin\frac{A}{2}} = \dfrac{p-a}{a}$.

Similarly, $\dfrac{\sin\frac{C}{2}\sin\frac{A}{2}}{\sin\frac{B}{2}} = \dfrac{p-b}{b}$ and $\dfrac{\sin\frac{A}{2}\sin\frac{B}{2}}{\sin\frac{C}{2}} = \dfrac{p-c}{c}$.

Then

$$\sqrt{\frac{\sin\frac{B}{2}\sin\frac{C}{2}}{\sin\frac{A}{2}}} + \sqrt{\frac{\sin\frac{C}{2}\sin\frac{A}{2}}{\sin\frac{B}{2}}} + \sqrt{\frac{\sin\frac{A}{2}\sin\frac{B}{2}}{\sin\frac{C}{2}}}$$

$$= \sqrt{\frac{p-a}{a}} + \sqrt{\frac{p-b}{b}} + \sqrt{\frac{p-c}{c}}$$

Moreover, $\sqrt{(p-a)a} \le \dfrac{p-a+a}{2} = \dfrac{p}{2}$.

It follows that

$$\left(\frac{p}{2}\right)\left(\frac{2}{p}\sqrt{\frac{p-a}{a}}\right) \ge \sqrt{(p-a)a}\left(\frac{2}{p}\sqrt{\frac{p-a}{a}}\right).$$

Then $\sqrt{\dfrac{p-a}{a}} \ge 2\left(\dfrac{p-a}{a}\right)$.

Similarly, $\sqrt{\dfrac{p-b}{b}} \ge 2\left(\dfrac{p-b}{p}\right)$ and $\sqrt{\dfrac{p-c}{c}} \ge 2\left(\dfrac{p-c}{p}\right)$.

Thus,

$$\sqrt{\frac{\sin\frac{B}{2}\sin\frac{C}{2}}{\sin\frac{A}{2}}} + \sqrt{\frac{\sin\frac{C}{2}\sin\frac{A}{2}}{\sin\frac{B}{2}}} + \sqrt{\frac{\sin\frac{A}{2}\sin\frac{B}{2}}{\sin\frac{C}{2}}}$$

$$\ge 2\left(\frac{p-a}{p} + \frac{p-b}{p} + \frac{p-c}{p}\right)$$

$$= 2$$

Therefore, $\dfrac{1}{\sin\frac{A}{2}} + \dfrac{1}{\sin\frac{B}{2}} + \dfrac{1}{\sin\frac{C}{2}} \ge 4\sqrt{\dfrac{R}{r}}$.

Problem 156. Suppose that m and n are two natural numbers. Let

$$S(m,n) = 1^m + 2^m + 3^m + \dots + n^m.$$

1. Prove that $C(m+1,1)S(m,n) + C(m+1,2)S(m-1,n) + \dots$
$$+ C(m+1,m)S(1,n) = (n+1)^{m+1} - (n+1).$$

2. Find $S(1,n)$ and $S(2,n)$ in terms of n.

3. For all real numbers k, let $[k]$ be the integer part of k. Compute

$$T_2 = \left[\sqrt{1}\right] + \left[\sqrt{2}\right] + \dots + \left[\sqrt{n^2-1}\right]$$

and

$$T_3 = \left[\sqrt[3]{1}\right] + \left[\sqrt[3]{2}\right] + \dots + \left[\sqrt[3]{n^3-1}\right]$$

in terms of n.

4. Let $T_k = \left[\sqrt[k]{1}\right] + \left[\sqrt[k]{2}\right] + ... + \left[\sqrt[k]{n^k - 1}\right]$. Prove that

$$T_k + S(k, n) = n^{k+1}.$$

Solution. 1. Prove that

$$C(m + 1, 1) S(m, n) + C(m + 1, 2) S(m - 1, n) + ...$$
$$+ C(m + 1, m) S(1, n) = (n + 1)^{m+1} - (n + 1).$$

Using Newton's theorem, we obtain

$$(k + 1)^{m+1} = k^{m+1} + C(m + 1, 1) k^m + ... + C(m + 1, m) k + 1.$$

Then

$$(k + 1)^{m+1} - k^{m+1} = C(m + 1, 1) k^m + ... + C(m + 1, m) k + 1.$$

Taking $k = 1, 2, 3, ...$ and n, it follows that

$$2^{m+1} - 1^{m+1} = C(m + 1, 1) 1^m + ... + C(m + 1, m) 1 + 1;$$
$$3^{m+1} - 2^{m+1} = C(m + 1, 1) 2^m + ... + C(m + 1, m) 2 + 1;$$
$$\vdots$$

and $(n + 1)^{m+1} - n^{m+1} = C(m + 1, 1) n^m + ...$
$$+ C(m + 1, m) n + 1.$$

Adding all of the above equalities, we obtain

$$(n + 1)^{m+1} - 1 = C(m + 1, 1) S(m, n) + ...$$
$$+ C(m + 1, m) S(1, n) + n.$$

Therefore, the identity is proved.

Remark 2. From the above computation, we obtain $S(m, n)$ is a polynomial in n of degree $m + 1$.

2. Compute $S(1, n)$ and $S(2, n)$.
We have

$$C(m + 1, 1) S(m, n) + C(m + 1, 2) S(m - 1, n) + ...$$

95

$$+ C\left(m+1, m\right) S\left(1, n\right) = \left(n+1\right)^{m+1} - \left(n+1\right).$$

For $m = 1$, we obtain

$$C\left(2, 1\right) S(1, n) = \left(n+1\right)^2 - \left(n+1\right).$$

Then

$$2S(1, n) = \left(n+1\right)\left(n+1-1\right) = n\left(n+1\right).$$

Therefore, $S(1, n) = \dfrac{n\left(n+1\right)}{2}.$

For $m = 2$, we obtain

$$C\left(3, 1\right) S(2, n) + C\left(3, 2\right) S(1, n) = \left(n+1\right)^3 - \left(n+1\right).$$

It follows that

$$3S(2, n) = \left(n+1\right)^3 - \left(n+1\right) - C\left(3, 2\right) S(1, n)$$
$$= \left(n+1\right)^3 - \left(n+1\right) - 3 \times \frac{n\left(n+1\right)}{2}$$
$$= \left(n+1\right)\left[\left(n+1\right)^2 - 1 - \frac{3}{2}n\right]$$
$$= \left(n+1\right) \times \frac{2(n+1)^2 - 2 - 3n}{2}$$
$$= \left(n+1\right) \times \frac{2\left(n^2 + 2n + 1\right) - 3n - 2}{2}$$
$$= \left(n+1\right) \times \frac{2n^2 + 4n + 2 - 3n - 2}{2}$$
$$= \left(n+1\right) \times \frac{2n^2 + n}{2}$$
$$= \frac{n\left(n+1\right)\left(2n+1\right)}{2}.$$

Thus, $S(2, n) = \dfrac{n\left(n+1\right)\left(2n+1\right)}{6}.$

3. • Compute T_2 in terms of n.

From the definition of integer part, if k is an integer that satisfies $n \leq \sqrt{k} < \sqrt{(n+1)^2 - 1}$, we obtain $\left[\sqrt{k}\right] = n$.

It is obvious to see that there are $(n+1)^2 - n^2$ numbers of k that satisfies the above condition. Hence,

$$T_2 = \left(\left[\sqrt{1}\right] + \left[\sqrt{2}\right] + \left[\sqrt{3}\right]\right) + \left(\left[\sqrt{4}\right] + \left[\sqrt{5}\right] + \left[\sqrt{6}\right]\right)$$

$$+ \dots$$

$$+ \left(\left[\sqrt{(n-1)^2}\right] + \left[\sqrt{(n-1)^2+1}\right] + \dots + \left[\sqrt{n^2-1}\right]\right)$$

$$+ \left(\sqrt{(n-1)^2} + \sqrt{(n-1)^2+1} + \dots + \sqrt{n^2-1}\right)$$

$$= 1\left(2^2 - 1^2\right) + 2\left(3^2 - 2^2\right) + \dots$$

$$+ (n-1)\left(n^2 - (n-1)^2\right)$$

$$= \left(2^2 - 1^2\right) + \left(2 \times 3^2 - 2 \times 2^2\right) + \dots$$

$$+ \left((n-1)n^2 - (n-1)(n-1)^2\right)$$

$$= -1^2 - 2^2 - \dots - (n-1)^2 + (n-1)n^2$$

$$= n^2(n-1) - \left(1^2 + 2^2 + \dots + (n-1)^2\right)$$

$$= n^2(n-1) - \frac{n(n-1)(2n-1)}{6}$$

$$= n(n-1)\left(n - \frac{2n-1}{6}\right)$$

$$= n(n-1)\left(\frac{6n - 2n + 1}{6}\right)$$

$$= n(n-1)\left(\frac{4n+1}{6}\right)$$

$$= \frac{n(n-1)(4n+1)}{6}$$

Thus, $T_2 = \dfrac{n(n-1)(4n+1)}{6}$.

- Compute T_3 in terms of n.

  By the definition of integer part, if k is an integer that satisfies $n \leq \sqrt[3]{k} < \sqrt[3]{(n+1)^3 - 1}$, it follows that $\left[\sqrt[3]{k}\right] = n$. It is obvious to see that there are $(n+1)^3 - n^3$ numbers of k that satisfies the above condition.

$$T_3 = \left(\left[\sqrt[3]{1} \right] + \left[\sqrt[3]{2} \right] + ... + \left[\sqrt[3]{7} \right] \right)$$
$$+ \left(\left[\sqrt[3]{8} \right] + \left[\sqrt[3]{9} \right] + ... + \left[\sqrt[3]{26} \right] \right)$$
$$+ ...$$
$$+ \left(\left[\sqrt[3]{(n-1)^3} \right] + \left[\sqrt[3]{(n-1)^3 + 1} \right] + ... + \left[\sqrt[3]{n^3 - 1} \right] \right)$$
$$= 1 \left(2^3 - 1^3 \right) + 2 \left(3^3 - 2^3 \right) + ... + (n-1) \left(n^3 - (n-1)^3 \right)$$
$$= -1^3 - 2^3 - ... - (n-1)^3 + n^3 (n-1)$$
$$= n^3 (n-1) - \left(1^3 + 2^3 + ... + (n-1)^3 \right)$$
$$= n^3 (n-1) - \left[\frac{n(n-1)}{2} \right]^2$$
$$= n^3 (n-1) - \frac{n^2 (n-1)^2}{4}$$
$$= n^2 (n-1) \left(n - \frac{n-1}{4} \right)$$
$$= \frac{n^2 (n-1)(4n - n + 1)}{4}$$
$$= \frac{n^2 (n-1)(3n+1)}{4}$$

$$\boxed{\text{Therefore, } T_3 = \frac{n^2 (n-1)(3n+1)}{4}.}$$

4. Prove that $T_k + S(k, n) = n^{k+1}$.

By the definition of integer part, if s is an integer that satisfies $n \le \sqrt[k]{s} < \sqrt[k]{(n+1)^k} - 1$, we obtain $\left[\sqrt[k]{s} \right] = n$. We can obviously see that there are $(n+1)^k - n^k$ numbers of s that satisfies the above condition. It follows that

$$T_k = \left(\left[\sqrt[k]{1} \right] + ... + \left[\sqrt[k]{2^k - 1} \right] \right) + \left(\left[\sqrt[k]{2^k} \right] + ... + \left[\sqrt[k]{3^k - 1} \right] \right)$$
$$+ ... + \left(\left[\sqrt[k]{(n-1)^k} \right] + ... + \left[\sqrt[k]{n^k - 1} \right] \right)$$
$$= 1 \times \left(2^k - 1^k \right) + 2 \left(3^k - 2^k \right) + ... + (n-1) \left(n^k - (n-1)^k \right)$$

$$= \left(1 \times 2^k - 1 \times 1^k\right) + \left(2 \times 3^k - 2 \times 2^k\right) + \dots$$
$$+ \left((n-1)\,n^k - (n-1)\,(n-1)^k\right)$$
$$= -1^k - 2^k - \dots - (n-1)^k + (n-1)\,n^k$$
$$= -1^k - 2^k - \dots - (n-1)^k - n^k + n^{k+1}$$
$$= n^{k+1} - \left(1^k + 2^k + \dots + n^k\right)$$
$$= n^{k+1} - S(k,n)$$

$$\boxed{\text{Hence, } T_k + S(k,n) = n^{k+1}.}$$

Problem 157. Given $\alpha \in \mathbb{R}$, $a \in \mathbb{Z}$ and $n \in \mathbb{N}$. Prove that

1. $[a + \alpha] = a + [\alpha]$;

2. $\left[\dfrac{\alpha}{n}\right] = \left[\dfrac{[\alpha]}{n}\right]$.

Solution. Prove that

1. $[a + \alpha] = a + [\alpha]$

   By the definition of integer part, we obtain
   $$[\alpha] \le \alpha < [\alpha] + 1.$$

   Then $[\alpha] + a \le \alpha + a < [\alpha] + a + 1$.

   $$\boxed{\text{Therefore, } [a + \alpha] = a + [\alpha].}$$

2. $\left[\dfrac{\alpha}{n}\right] = \left[\dfrac{[\alpha]}{n}\right]$

   - If α is an integer, we obtain $[\alpha] = \alpha$.

     Then $\left[\dfrac{[\alpha]}{n}\right] = \left[\dfrac{\alpha}{n}\right]$

   - If α is not an integer, then
     $$\left[\frac{\alpha}{n}\right] \le \frac{\alpha}{n} < \left[\frac{\alpha}{n}\right] + 1.$$

   We obtain $n\left[\dfrac{\alpha}{n}\right] \le \alpha < n\left[\dfrac{\alpha}{n}\right] + n$.

   It follows that $n\left[\dfrac{\alpha}{n}\right] \le [\alpha] < n\left[\dfrac{\alpha}{n}\right] + n$.

   Divide both side of the above inequality by n, we obtain
   $$\left[\frac{\alpha}{n}\right] \le \frac{[\alpha]}{n} < \left[\frac{\alpha}{n}\right] + 1.$$

Thus, $\left[\dfrac{[\alpha]}{n}\right] = \left[\dfrac{\alpha}{n}\right]$.

Therefore, $\left[\dfrac{\alpha}{n}\right] = \left[\dfrac{[\alpha]}{n}\right]$.

Problem 158. Given x, y and z are three real numbers. Prove that

1. $2\left([x] + [y] + [z]\right) \le [x + y] + [y + z] + [z + x]$
$$\le 2\left([x] + [y] + [z]\right) + 3;$$

2. $2\left([x] + [y] + [z]\right)$
$$\le 2\left([2x] + [2y] + [2z]\right) - [x + y] - [y + z] - [z + x].$$

Solution. To prove the given inequalities, we first prove the following lemma:

Lemma 1. For all real numbers α and β, we obtain the following inequalities:

1. $[\alpha] + [\beta] \le [\alpha + \beta] \le [\alpha] + [\beta] + 1$;

2. $[\alpha] + [\beta] + [\alpha + \beta] \le [2\alpha] + [2\beta]$.

Proof. Prove that

1. $[\alpha] + [\beta] \le [\alpha + \beta] \le [\alpha] + [\beta] + 1$
   By the definition of integer part, we have $[\alpha] \le \alpha$ and $[\beta] \le \beta$.
   Then $[\alpha] + [\beta] \le \alpha + \beta$.
   Hence,
   $$[\alpha] + [\beta] \le [\alpha + \beta]. \tag{1}$$
   Moreover, $\alpha = [\alpha] + \{\alpha\}$ and $\beta = [\beta] + \{\beta\}$. It follows that
   $$\alpha + \beta = [\alpha] + [\beta] + \{\alpha\} + \{\beta\}.$$

As a result, $\begin{aligned}[\alpha + \beta] &= [[\alpha] + [\beta] + \{\alpha\} + \{\beta\}] \\ &= [\alpha] + [\beta] + [\{\alpha\} + \{\beta\}].\end{aligned}$

Since $0 \le \{\alpha\}, \{\beta\} < 1$, it follows that $0 \le \{\alpha\} + \{\beta\} < 2$.
Consequently, $[\{\alpha\} + \{\beta\}] \le 1$.
It follows that
$$[\alpha + \beta] \le [\alpha] + [\beta] + 1. \tag{2}$$
From (1) and (2), we obtain $[\alpha] + [\beta] \le [\alpha + \beta] \le [\alpha] + [\beta] + 1$.

Therefore, $[\alpha] + [\beta] \le [\alpha + \beta] \le [\alpha] + [\beta] + 1$.

2. $[\alpha] + [\beta] + [\alpha + \beta] \leq [2\alpha] + [2\beta]$

By the definition of integer part, we have

$$\alpha = \{\alpha\} + [\alpha]$$

and

$$\beta = \{\beta\} + [\beta].$$

We have

$$[\alpha] + [\beta] + [\alpha + \beta] = [\alpha] + [\beta] + [[\alpha] + \{\alpha\} + [\beta] + \{\beta\}]$$
$$= [\alpha] + [\beta] + [\alpha] + [\beta] + [\{\alpha\} + \{\beta\}]$$
$$= 2[\alpha] + 2[\beta] + [\{\alpha\} + \{\beta\}].$$

Moreover,

$$[2\alpha] + [2\beta] = [2([\alpha] + \{\alpha\})] + [2([\beta] + \{\beta\})]$$
$$= [2[\alpha] + 2\{\alpha\}] + [2[\beta] + 2\{\beta\}]$$
$$= 2[\alpha] + 2[\beta] + [2\{\alpha\}] + [2\{\beta\}].$$

It follows that

$$([2\alpha] + [2\beta]) - ([\alpha] + [\beta] + [\alpha + \beta])$$
$$= (2[\alpha] + 2[\beta] + [2\{\alpha\}] + [2\{\beta\}])$$
$$- (2[\alpha] + 2[\beta] + [\{\alpha\} + \{\beta\}])$$
$$= [2\{\alpha\}] + [2\{\beta\}] - [\{\alpha\} + \{\beta\}].$$

Without loss of generality, we may assume that

$$1 > \{\alpha\} \geq \{\beta\} \geq 0.$$

We obtain $[2\{\alpha\}] + [2\{\beta\}] \geq [2\{\alpha\}] \geq [\{\alpha\} + \{\beta\}]$.

Then $([2\alpha] + [2\beta]) - ([\alpha] + [\beta] + [\alpha + \beta]) \geq 0$.

Therefore, $[\alpha] + [\beta] + [\alpha + \beta] \leq [2\alpha] + [2\beta].$

□

Prove the following inequalities:

1. $2([x] + [y] + [z]) \leq [x + y] + [y + z] + [z + x]$
$$\leq 2([x] + [y] + [z]) + 3$$

From the above lemma, we have

$$[\alpha] + [\beta] \leq [\alpha + \beta] \leq [\alpha] + [\beta] + 1$$

for all real numbers α and β. Hence, for all real numbers x, y and z, we obtain

$$[x] + [y] \le [x + y] \le [x] + [y] + 1;$$
$$[y] + [z] \le [y + z] \le [y] + [z] + 1;$$
and $\quad [z] + [x] \le [z + x] \le [z] + [x] + 1.$

Adding all of the above inequalities, we obtain
$$2\,([x] + [y] + [z]) \le [x + y] + [y + z] + [z + x]$$
$$\le 2\,([x] + [y] + [z]) + 3.$$

Therefore, $2\,([x] + [y] + [z]) \le [x + y] + [y + z] + [z + x]$
$$\le 2\,([x] + [y] + [z]) + 3.$$

2. $2\,([x] + [y] + [z]) \le [2x] + [2y] + [2z] - [x + y] - [y + z] - [z + x]$
Using the above lemma, we have

$$[\alpha] + [\beta] + [\alpha + \beta] \le [2\alpha] + [2\beta]$$

for all real numbers α and β. It follows that

$$[\alpha] + [\beta] \le [2\alpha] + [2\beta] - [\alpha + \beta].$$

For all real numbers x, y and z, we have

$$[x] + [y] \le [2x] + [2y] - [x + y]$$
$$[y] + [z] \le [2y] + [2z] - [y + z]$$
and $\quad [z] + [x] \le [2z] + [2x] - [z + x]$

Adding all of the above inequalities, we have

$$2\,([x] + [y] + [z]) \le 2\,([2x] + [2y] + [2z]) - [x + y] - [y + z] - [z + x].$$

Therefore, $2\,([x] + [y] + [z])$
$$\le 2\,([2x] + [2y] + [2z]) - [x + y] - [y + z] - [z + x].$$

Problem 159. For all real numbers x and positive integers n, prove that

1. $\dfrac{n\,(n + 1)}{2}\,[x] \le [x] + [2x] + \ldots + [nx] \le \dfrac{n\,(n + 1)}{2}\,([x] + 1) - n;$

2. $n + \dfrac{n\,(n + 1)}{2}\,(\{x\} - 1) \le \{x\} + \{2x\} + \ldots + \{nx\} \le \dfrac{n\,(n + 1)}{2}\,\{x\}.$

Solution.

Lemma 2. Given a real number x and positive integer n, prove that

1. $0 \leq [nx] - n[x] \leq n - 1$;

2. $1 - n \leq \{nx\} - n\{x\} \leq 0$.

Proof. Prove that

1. $0 \leq [nx] - n[x] \leq n - 1$

   We have
   $$[nx] - n[x] = [nx - n[x]]$$
   $$= [n(x - [x])]$$
   $$= [n\{x\}].$$

   Since $0 \leq \{x\} < 1$, it follows that $0 \leq n\{x\} < n$.
   We obtain $0 \leq [n\{x\}] \leq n - 1$.

   $\boxed{\text{Therefore, } 0 \leq [nx] - n[x] \leq n - 1.}$

2. $1 - n \leq \{nx\} - n\{x\} \leq 0$
   We have $\{nx\} = nx - [nx]$ and $\{x\} = x - [x]$.
   From the above lemma, we have $0 \leq [nx] - n[x] \leq n - 1$.

   It follows that
   $$0 \leq (nx - \{nx\}) - n(x - \{x\}) \leq n - 1$$
   $$0 \leq nx - \{nx\} - nx + n\{x\} \leq n - 1$$
   $$0 \leq -\{nx\} + n\{x\} \leq n - 1$$
   $$0 \leq -(\{nx\} - n\{x\}) \leq n - 1$$
   $$1 - n \leq \{nx\} - n\{x\} \leq 0.$$

   $\boxed{\text{Therefore, } 1 - n \leq \{nx\} - n\{x\} \leq 0.}$

   $\square$

Prove that

1. $\dfrac{n(n+1)}{2}[x] \leq [x] + [2x] + \ldots + [nx] \leq \dfrac{n(n+1)}{2}([x] + 1) - 1$
   From the above lemma, $0 \leq [kx] - k[x] \leq k - 1$. It implies that
   $$k[x] \leq [kx] \leq k[x] + k - 1$$

or

$$k[x] \le [kx] \le k([x]+1) - 1.$$

Hence, $[x] \sum_{k=1}^{n} k \le \sum_{k=1}^{n} [kx] \le \sum_{k=1}^{n} (k([x]+1) - 1).$

Then $[x] \sum_{k=1}^{n} k \le \sum_{k=1}^{n} [kx] \le ([x]+1) \sum_{k=1}^{n} k - \sum_{k=1}^{n} 1.$

It follows that

$$\frac{n(n+1)}{2}[x] \le \sum_{k=1}^{n} [kx] \le \frac{n(n+1)}{2}([x]+1) - n.$$

Therefore, $\dfrac{n(n+1)}{2}[x] \le [x] + [2x] + ... + [nx]$

$$\le \frac{n(n+1)}{2}([x]+1) - n.$$

2. $n + \dfrac{n(n+1)}{2}(\{x\} - 1) \le \{x\} + \{2x\} + ... + \{nx\} \le \dfrac{n(n+1)}{2}\{x\}$

From the above lemma, we have

$$1 - k \le \{kx\} - k\{x\} \le 0.$$

Then

$$1 - k + k\{x\} \le \{kx\} \le k\{x\}.$$

It follows that

$$1 + k(\{x\} - 1) \le \{kx\} \le k\{x\}.$$

We obtain

$$\sum_{k=1}^{n} (1 + k(\{x\} - 1)) \le \sum_{k=1}^{n} \{kx\} \le \sum_{k=1}^{n} k\{x\}.$$

Then

$$\sum_{k=1}^{n} 1 + (\{x\} - 1) \sum_{k=1}^{n} k \le \sum_{k=1}^{n} \{kx\} \le \{x\} \sum_{k=1}^{n} k.$$

Thus,

$$n + \frac{n(n+1)}{2}(\{x\} - 1) \le \sum_{k=1}^{n} \{kx\} \le \frac{n(n+1)}{2}\{x\}.$$

Therefore, $n + \dfrac{n(n+1)}{2}(\{x\} - 1)$

$$\leq \{x\} + \{2x\} + ... + \{nx\} \leq \dfrac{n(n+1)}{2}\{x\}.$$

Problem 160. Given two positive real numbers α and β which are not an integer. Prove the following inequalities:

1. $\dfrac{\alpha}{\{\alpha\}} + \dfrac{\beta}{\{\beta\}} \geq 2$;

2. $\alpha^2\left(\left[\dfrac{\beta}{\alpha^2}\right] + 1\right) + \beta^2\left(\left[\dfrac{\alpha}{\beta^2}\right] + 1\right) > \alpha + \beta$;

3. $[\alpha][\beta] \leq [\alpha\beta] \leq [\alpha][\beta] + [\alpha] + [\beta]$.

Solution. Prove the following inequalities:

1. $\dfrac{\alpha}{\{\alpha\}} + \dfrac{\beta}{\{\beta\}} \geq 2$

   By definition of integer part, we have $\alpha = [\alpha] + \{\alpha\}$ and $\beta = [\beta] + \{\beta\}$. Then

$$\dfrac{\alpha}{\{\alpha\}} + \dfrac{\beta}{\{\beta\}} = \dfrac{\{\alpha\} + [\alpha]}{\{\alpha\}} + \dfrac{\{\beta\} + [\beta]}{\{\beta\}}$$

$$= \dfrac{\{\alpha\}}{\{\alpha\}} + \dfrac{[\alpha]}{\{\alpha\}} + \dfrac{\{\beta\}}{\{\beta\}} + \dfrac{[\beta]}{\{\beta\}}$$

$$= 1 + \dfrac{[\alpha]}{\{\alpha\}} + 1 + \dfrac{[\beta]}{\{\beta\}}$$

$$= 2 + \dfrac{[\alpha]}{\{\alpha\}} + \dfrac{[\beta]}{\{\beta\}}.$$

By knowing that $\alpha, \beta \notin \mathbb{Z}$ and both are positive real numbers, then $0 < \{\alpha\}, \{\beta\} < 1$ and $[\alpha], [\beta] \geq 0$.

Then $\dfrac{[\alpha]}{\{\alpha\}} + \dfrac{[\beta]}{\{\beta\}} \geq 0$. The equality holds if and only if $[\alpha] = [\beta] = 0$.

Therefore, $\dfrac{\alpha}{\{\alpha\}} + \dfrac{\beta}{\{\beta\}} \geq 2.$

2. $\alpha^2\left(\left[\dfrac{\beta}{\alpha^2}\right] + 1\right) + \beta^2\left(\left[\dfrac{\alpha}{\beta^2}\right] + 1\right) > \alpha + \beta$

   By definition of integer part, we have $\left[\dfrac{\beta}{\alpha^2}\right] > \dfrac{\beta}{\alpha^2} - 1$.

Multiply both sides of the inequality by α^2, it follows that

$$\alpha^2 \left[\frac{\beta}{\alpha^2}\right] > \beta - \alpha^2.$$

Then $\alpha^2 \left[\dfrac{\beta}{\alpha^2}\right] + \alpha^2 > \beta$

Hence,

$$\alpha^2 \left(\left[\frac{\beta}{\alpha^2}\right] + 1\right) > \beta. \tag{1}$$

Similarly, we obtain

$$\beta^2 \left(\left[\frac{\alpha}{\beta^2}\right] + 1\right) > \alpha \tag{2}$$

From (1) and (2), it implies that

$$\alpha^2 \left(\left[\frac{\beta}{\alpha^2}\right] + 1\right) + \beta^2 \left(\left[\frac{\alpha}{\beta^2}\right] + 1\right) > \alpha + \beta$$

$$\boxed{\text{Therefore, } \alpha^2 \left(\left[\frac{\beta}{\alpha^2}\right] + 1\right) + \beta^2 \left(\left[\frac{\alpha}{\beta^2}\right] + 1\right) > \alpha + \beta.}$$

3. $[\alpha][\beta] \leq [\alpha\beta] \leq [\alpha][\beta] + [\alpha] + [\beta]$
   By the definition of integer part, we have $\alpha = [\alpha] + \{\alpha\}$ and $\beta = [\beta] + \{\beta\}$. It follows that

$$
\begin{aligned}
[\alpha\beta] &= [([\alpha] + \{\alpha\})([\beta] + \{\beta\})] \\
&= [[\alpha][\beta] + [\alpha]\{\beta\} + \{\alpha\}[\beta] + \{\alpha\}\{\beta\}] \\
&= [\alpha][\beta] + [[\alpha]\{\beta\} + \{\alpha\}[\beta] + \{\alpha\}\{\beta\}].
\end{aligned}
$$

By knowing that $\alpha, \beta \notin \mathbb{Z}$ and both are positive real numbers, it implies that $0 < \{\alpha\}, \{\beta\} < 1$.
Then $[\alpha]\{\beta\} + \{\alpha\}[\beta] + \{\alpha\}\{\beta\} > 0$.
It follows that $[[\alpha]\{\beta\} + \{\alpha\}[\beta] + \{\alpha\}\{\beta\}] \geq 0$.
Hence,

$$[\alpha\beta] \geq [\alpha][\beta]. \tag{1}$$

Moreover, $\{\alpha\}, \{\beta\} < 1$. Then $[\alpha]\{\beta\} + [\beta]\{\alpha\} < [\alpha] + [\beta]$.
Then $[[\alpha]\{\beta\} + [\beta]\{\alpha\}] \leq [\alpha] + [\beta]$. It turns out that

$$[\alpha\beta] \leq [\alpha][\beta] + [[\alpha] + [\beta] + \{\alpha\}\{\beta\}]$$

$$= [\alpha][\beta] + [\alpha] + [\beta] + [\{\alpha\}\{\beta\}]$$
$$= [\alpha][\beta] + [\alpha] + [\beta]. \tag{2}$$

From (1) and (2), we obtain $[\alpha][\beta] \leq [\alpha\beta] \leq [\alpha][\beta]+[\alpha]+[\beta]$.

$\boxed{\text{Therefore, } [\alpha][\beta] \leq [\alpha\beta] \leq [\alpha][\beta] + [\alpha] + [\beta].}$

Problem 161. Let $[x]$ be the integer part of x. For all positive integers n, prove that

1. $A = \left[\cos^{2n-1}1°\right] + \left[\cos^{2n-1}2°\right] + ... + \left[\cos^{2n-1}180°\right]$;

2. $B = \left[\sin^{2n-1}1°\right] + \left[\sin^{2n-1}2°\right] + ... + \left[\sin^{2n-1}360°\right]$.

Solution. Before proving the given inequality, we first prove the following lemma:

Lemma 3. • If $x \in \mathbb{Z}$, we obtain $[x] + [-x] = 0$.

• If $x \notin \mathbb{Z}$, we obtain $[x] + [-x] = -1$.

Proof. • If $x \in \mathbb{Z}$, it follows that $[x] + [-x] = x - x = 0$.

• If $x \notin \mathbb{Z}$, let $k = [x]$, it turns out that $k < x < k + 1$. Hence, $-k - 1 < -x < -k$.
Then $[-x] = -k - 1$.
Hence, $[x] + [-x] = k - k - 1 = -1$. $\qquad\square$

Let's now get back to compute the given sums.

1. $A = \left[\cos^{2n-1}1°\right] + \left[\cos^{2n-1}2°\right] + ... + \left[\cos^{2n-1}180°\right]$
We have $\cos(180° - x) = -\cos x$.
Then $\cos^{2n-1}(180° - x) = (-\cos x)^{2n-1} = -\cos^{2n-1}x$.
Hence, A can be written as

$$\left(\left[\cos^{2n-1}1°\right] + \left[\cos^{2n-1}2°\right] + ... + \left[\cos^{2n-1}90°\right]\right)$$
$$+ \left(\left[\cos^{2n-1}91°\right] + \left[\cos^{2n-1}92°\right] + ... + \left[\cos^{2n-1}180°\right]\right)$$
$$= \left(\left[\cos^{2n-1}1°\right] + \left[\cos^{2n-1}2°\right] + ... + \left[\cos^{2n-1}90°\right]\right)$$
$$+ \left(\left[-\cos^{2n-1}89°\right] + \left[-\cos^{2n-1}88°\right] + ... + \left[-\cos^{2n-1}0°\right]\right)$$
$$= \left(\left[\cos^{2n-1}1°\right] + \left[\cos^{2n-1}2°\right] + ... + \left[\cos^{2n-1}89°\right] + [0]\right)$$
$$+ \left(\left[-\cos^{2n-1}89°\right] + \left[-\cos^{2n-1}88°\right] + ... + \left[-\cos^{2n-1}1°\right] + [-1]\right)$$
$$= \left(\left[\cos^{2n-1}1°\right] + \left[-\cos^{2n-1}1°\right]\right)$$

$$+ \left(\left[\cos^{2n-1} 2^\circ \right] + \left[-\cos^{2n-1} 2^\circ \right] \right) + \dots$$
$$+ \left(\left[\cos^{2n-1} 89^\circ \right] + \left[-\cos^{2n-1} 89^\circ \right] \right) - 1$$
$$= \underbrace{-1 - 1 - \dots - 1}_{89} - 1$$
$$= -90.$$

Therefore, $A = -90$.

2. $B = \left[\sin^{2n-1} 1^\circ \right] + \left[\sin^{2n-1} 2^\circ \right] + \dots + \left[\sin^{2n-1} 360^\circ \right]$
We have $\sin(180^\circ + x) = -\sin x$.
Then

$$B = \left[\sin^{2n-1} 1^\circ \right] + \left[\sin^{2n-1} 2^\circ \right] + \dots + \left[\sin^{2n-1} 360^\circ \right]$$
$$= \left(\left[\sin^{2n-1} 1^\circ \right] + \left[\sin^{2n-1} 2^\circ \right] + \dots + \left[\sin^{2n-1} 180^\circ \right] \right)$$
$$+ \left(\left[\sin^{2n-1} 181^\circ \right] + \left[\sin^{2n-1} 182^\circ \right] + \dots + \left[\sin^{2n-1} 360^\circ \right] \right)$$
$$= \left(\left[\sin^{2n-1} 1^\circ \right] + \left[\sin^{2n-1} 2^\circ \right] + \dots + \left[\sin^{2n-1} 180^\circ \right] \right)$$
$$+ \left(\left[-\sin^{2n-1} 1^\circ \right] + \left[-\sin^{2n-1} 2^\circ \right] + \dots + \left[-\sin^{2n-1} 180^\circ \right] \right)$$
$$= \left(\left[\sin^{2n-1} 1^\circ \right] + \left[-\sin^{2n-1} 1^\circ \right] \right) + \left(\left[\sin^{2n-1} 2^\circ \right] + \left[-\sin^{2n-1} 2^\circ \right] \right)$$
$$+ \dots + \left(\left[\sin^{2n-1} 180^\circ \right] + \left[-\sin^{2n-1} 180^\circ \right] \right).$$

By knowing that $\left[\sin^{2n-1} 90^\circ \right] + \left[-\sin^{2n-1} 90^\circ \right]$
$$= \left[\sin^{2n-1} 180^\circ \right] + \left[-\sin^{2n-1} 180^\circ \right]$$
$$= 0,$$
we obtain

$$B = \left(\underbrace{-1 - 1 - \dots - 1}_{89} \right) + \left(\underbrace{-1 - 1 - \dots - 1}_{89} \right)$$
$$= -178.$$

Therefore, $B = -178$.

Problem 162. Let $\{x\}$ be the fractional part of x and n be a positive integer. Compute the following sums:

1. $S = \left\{ \cos^{2n-1} 1^\circ \right\} + \left\{ \cos^{2n-1} 2^\circ \right\} + \dots + \left\{ \cos^{2n-1} 180^\circ \right\}$;

2. $T = \left\{ \sin^{2n-1} 1^\circ \right\} + \left\{ \sin^{2n-1} 2^\circ \right\} + \dots + \left\{ \sin^{2n-1} 360^\circ \right\}$.

Solution. Let's us first prove the following lemma:

Lemma 4. For all real numbers x such that $x \notin \mathbb{Z}$, we obtain

$$\{x\} + \{-x\} = 1.$$

Proof. We have $\{x\} = x - [x]$ and $\{-x\} = -x - [-x]$. It follows that

$$\begin{aligned}
\{x\} + \{-x\} &= (x - [x]) + (-x - [-x]) \\
&= x - [x] - x - [-x] \\
&= -([x] + [-x]).
\end{aligned}$$

Since $[x] + [-x] = -1$ for all $x \notin \mathbb{Z}$, we obtain

$$\{x\} + \{-x\} = -(-1) = 1.$$

Thus, the lemma is proved. $\qquad\square$

From the above lemma, we can compute the given sums as the following:

1. $S = \left\{\cos^{2n-1} 1^\circ\right\} + \left\{\cos^{2n-1} 2^\circ\right\} + \ldots + \left\{\cos^{2n-1} 180^\circ\right\}$
   Using $\cos(180^\circ - x) = -\cos x$, we obtain

$$\begin{aligned}
\cos^{2n-1}(180^\circ - x) &= (-\cos x)^{2n-1} \\
&= (-1)^{2n-1} \cos^{2n-1} x \\
&= -\cos^{2n-1} x.
\end{aligned}$$

It follows that

$$\begin{aligned}
S &= \left\{\cos^{2n-1} 1^\circ\right\} + \left\{\cos^{2n-1} 2^\circ\right\} + \ldots + \left\{\cos^{2n-1} 180^\circ\right\} \\
&= \left(\left\{\cos^{2n-1} 1^\circ\right\} + \left\{\cos^{2n-1} 2^\circ\right\} + \ldots + \left\{\cos^{2n-1} 90^\circ\right\}\right) \\
&\quad + \left(\left\{-\cos^{2n-1} 1^\circ\right\} + \left\{-\cos^{2n-1} 2^\circ\right\} + \ldots + \left\{-\cos^{2n-1} 90^\circ\right\}\right) \\
&= \left(\left\{\cos^{2n-1} 1^\circ\right\} + \left\{-\cos^{2n-1} 1^\circ\right\}\right) \\
&\quad + \left(\left\{\cos^{2n-1} 2^\circ\right\} + \left\{-\cos^{2n-1} 2^\circ\right\}\right) + \ldots \\
&\quad + \left(\left\{\cos^{2n-1} 89^\circ\right\} + \left\{-\cos^{2n-1} 89^\circ\right\}\right) + \left\{\cos^{2n-1} 90^\circ\right\} \\
&\quad + \left\{-\cos^{2n-1} 90^\circ\right\} \\
&= \underbrace{1 + 1 + \ldots + 1}_{89} + \{1\} + \{-1\}
\end{aligned}$$

$$= 89 + 0 + 0$$
$$= 89.$$

Therefore, $S = 89.$

2. $T = \left\{\sin^{2n-1}1^\circ\right\} + \left\{\sin^{2n-1}2^\circ\right\} + \ldots + \left\{\sin^{2n-1}360^\circ\right\}$
Using the formula $\sin\left(180^\circ + x\right) = -\sin x$, we obtain

$$T = \left\{\sin^{2n-1}1^\circ\right\} + \left\{\sin^{2n-1}2^\circ\right\} + \ldots + \left\{\sin^{2n-1}360^\circ\right\}$$
$$= \left\{\sin^{2n-1}1^\circ\right\} + \left\{\sin^{2n-1}2^\circ\right\} + \ldots + \left\{\sin^{2n-1}180^\circ\right\}$$
$$+ \left\{-\sin^{2n-1}1^\circ\right\} + \left\{-\sin^{2n-1}2^\circ\right\} + \ldots + \left\{-\sin^{2n-1}180^\circ\right\}$$
$$= \left(\left\{\sin^{2n-1}1^\circ\right\} + \left\{-\sin^{2n-1}1^\circ\right\}\right)$$
$$+ \left(\left\{\sin^{2n-1}2^\circ\right\} + \left\{-\sin^{2n-1}2^\circ\right\}\right)$$
$$+ \ldots + \left(\left\{\sin^{2n-1}89^\circ\right\} + \left\{-\sin^{2n-1}89^\circ\right\}\right)$$
$$+ \left(\left\{\sin 91^\circ\right\} + \left\{-\sin 91^\circ\right\}\right)$$
$$+ \left(\left\{\sin 92^\circ\right\} + \left\{-\sin 92^\circ\right\}\right) + \ldots + \left(\left\{\sin 179^\circ\right\} + \left\{-\sin 179^\circ\right\}\right)$$
$$= \underbrace{1 + 1 + \ldots + 1}_{178}$$
$$= 178.$$

Therefore, $T = 178.$

Problem 163. Compute the following sums:

1. $S_1 = \left[\dfrac{1^2 + 2^2}{2}\right] + \left[\dfrac{2^2 + 3^2}{2^2}\right] + \ldots + \left[\dfrac{n^2 + (n+1)^2}{2}\right]$;

2. $S_2 = \left[\dfrac{1^2 + 2^2 + 3^2}{3}\right] + \left[\dfrac{2^2 + 3^2 + 4^2}{3}\right] + \ldots$
$$+ \left[\dfrac{n^2 + (n+1)^2 + (n+2)^2}{3}\right].$$

Solution.   1. $S_1 = \left[\dfrac{1^2 + 2^2}{2}\right] + \left[\dfrac{2^2 + 3^2}{2^2}\right] + \ldots + \left[\dfrac{n^2 + (n+1)^2}{2}\right]$

To compute the given sum, we first observe the kth term of the given sums. Try to write it as a telescoping sum. For all

110

positive integers k, we have

$$\left[\frac{k^2 + (k+1)^2}{2}\right] = \left[\frac{k^2 + k^2 + 2k + 1}{2}\right]$$

$$= \left[\frac{2k^2 + 2k + 1}{2}\right]$$

$$= \left[\frac{2k^2}{2} + \frac{2k}{2} + \frac{1}{2}\right]$$

$$= \left[k^2 + k + \frac{1}{2}\right]$$

$$= k^2 + k$$

We obtain

$$S_1 = \sum_{k=1}^{n}\left[\frac{k^2 + (k+1)^2}{2}\right]$$

$$= \sum_{k=1}^{n}(k^2 + k)$$

$$= \sum_{k=1}^{n}k^2 + \sum_{k=1}^{n}k$$

$$= \frac{n(n+1)(2n+1)}{6} + \frac{n(n+1)}{2}$$

$$= \frac{n(n+1)}{6}[(2n+1) + 3]$$

$$= \frac{n(n+1)}{6} \times (2n+4)$$

$$= \frac{n(n+1)}{6} \times 2(n+2)$$

$$= \frac{n(n+1)(n+2)}{3}.$$

Therefore, $S_1 = \dfrac{n(n+1)(n+2)}{3}$.

2. $S_2 = \left[\dfrac{1^2 + 2^2 + 3^2}{3}\right] + \left[\dfrac{2^2 + 3^2 + 4^2}{3}\right] + \ldots$

$$+ \left[\frac{n^2 + (n+1)^2 + (n+2)^2}{3}\right]$$

For all positive integers k, we have

$$\left[\frac{k^2 + (k+1)^2 + (k+2)^2}{3}\right] = \left[\frac{k^2 + k^2 + 2k + 1 + k^2 + 4k + 4}{3}\right]$$

$$= \left[\frac{3k^2 + 6k + 5}{3}\right]$$

$$= \left[\frac{3k^2}{3} + \frac{6k}{3} + \frac{5}{3}\right]$$

$$= \left[k^2 + 2k + 1 + \frac{2}{3}\right]$$

$$= \left[(k+1)^2 + \frac{2}{3}\right]$$

$$= (k+1)^2.$$

As a result,

$$S_2 = \sum_{k=1}^{n}\left[\frac{k^2 + (k+1)^2 + (k+2)^2}{3}\right]$$

$$= \sum_{k=1}^{n}(k+1)^2$$

$$= \sum_{k=2}^{n+1} k^2$$

$$= \sum_{k=1}^{n+1} k^2 - 1$$

$$= \frac{(n+1)(n+1+1)(2(n+1)+1)}{6} - 1$$

$$= \frac{(n+1)(n+2)(2n+3)}{6} - 1.$$

Therefore, $S_2 = \dfrac{(n+1)(n+2)(2n+3)}{6} - 1.$

Problem 164. Given a and b are two integers. Let $[x]$ be the integer part of x. Prove that $\left[\dfrac{a^2 + b^2}{2}\right] + \left[\dfrac{a^2 - b^2}{2}\right]$ does not depend on the choice of b.

Solution. Prove that $\left[\dfrac{a^2+b^2}{2}\right] + \left[\dfrac{a^2-b^2}{2}\right]$ does not depend on the choice of b.

If a and b have the same parity, then a^2 and b^2 also have the same parity.

We obtain a^2+b^2 and a^2-b^2 are both even integer. In this case, we obtain $\dfrac{a^2+b^2}{2}$ and $\dfrac{a^2-b^2}{2}$ are both integer. We obtain

$$
\begin{aligned}
\left[\frac{a^2+b^2}{2}\right] + \left[\frac{a^2-b^2}{2}\right] &= \frac{a^2+b^2}{2} + \frac{a^2-b^2}{2} \\
&= \frac{a^2+b^2+a^2-b^2}{2} \\
&= \frac{2a^2}{2} \\
&= a^2.
\end{aligned}
$$

We obviously see that $\left[\dfrac{a^2+b^2}{2}\right] + \left[\dfrac{a^2-b^2}{2}\right]$ does not depend on the choice of b in this case. Hence, to prove the given statement, it is sufficient to prove it in the case a and b have different parity.

- If a is even and b is odd, then there exists integers k_1 and k_2 such that $a = 2k_1$ and $b = 2k_2 + 1$. It follows that

$$
\begin{aligned}
&\left[\frac{a^2+b^2}{2}\right] + \left[\frac{a^2-b^2}{2}\right] \\
&= \left[\frac{(2k_1)^2 + (2k_2+1)^2}{2}\right] + \left[\frac{(2k_1)^2 - (2k_2+1)^2}{2}\right] \\
&= \left[\frac{4k_1^2 + 4k_2^2 + 4k_2 + 1}{2}\right] + \left[\frac{4k_1^2 - 4k_2^2 - 4k_2 - 1}{2}\right] \\
&= \left[2k_1^2 + 2k_2^2 + 2k_2 + \frac{1}{2}\right] + \left[2k_1^2 - 2k_2^2 - 2k_2 + \frac{1}{2}\right] \\
&= 2k_1^2 + 2k_2^2 + 2k_2 + 2k_1^2 - 2k_2^2 - 2k_2 \\
&= 4k_1^2 \\
&= (2k_1)^2 \\
&= a^2.
\end{aligned}
$$

It is obvious to see that $\left[\dfrac{a^2 + b^2}{2}\right] + \left[\dfrac{a^2 - b^2}{2}\right]$ does not depend on b in this case.

- If a is odd and b is even, then there exists integers k_1 and k_2 such that $a = 2k_1 + 1$ and $b = 2k_2$. It turns out that

$$\left[\dfrac{a^2 + b^2}{2}\right] + \left[\dfrac{a^2 - b^2}{2}\right]$$

$$= \left[\dfrac{(2k_1 + 1)^2 + (2k_2)^2}{2}\right] + \left[\dfrac{(2k_1 + 1)^2 - (2k_2)^2}{2}\right]$$

$$= \left[\dfrac{4k_1^2 + 4k_1 + 1 + 4k_2^2}{2}\right] + \left[\dfrac{4k_1^2 + 4k_1 + 1 - 4k_2^2}{2}\right]$$

$$= \left[2k_1^2 + 2k_1 + 2k_2^2 + \dfrac{1}{2}\right] + \left[2k_1^2 + 2k_1 - 2k_2^2 + \dfrac{1}{2}\right]$$

$$= 2k_1^2 + 2k_1 + 2k_2^2 + 2k_1^2 + 2k_1 - 2k_2^2$$

$$= 4k_1^2 + 4k_1$$

$$= \left(4k_1^2 + 4k_1 + 1\right) - 1$$

$$= (2k_1 + 1)^2 - 1$$

$$= a^2 - 1.$$

It is obvious to see that $\left[\dfrac{a^2 + b^2}{2}\right] + \left[\dfrac{a^2 - b^2}{2}\right]$ does not depend on b in this case.

Therefore, $\left[\dfrac{a^2 + b^2}{2}\right] + \left[\dfrac{a^2 - b^2}{2}\right]$ does not depend on b.

Problem 165.   1. Given that k is an integer. Prove that

$$\left[\dfrac{k}{2}\right] + \left[\dfrac{k + 1}{2}\right] = k.$$

2. Compute $S = \left[\dfrac{1}{2}\right] + \left[\dfrac{2}{2}\right] + ... + \left[\dfrac{n}{2}\right].$

Solution.   1. Prove that $\left[\dfrac{k}{2}\right] + \left[\dfrac{k + 1}{2}\right] = k.$

To prove the given statement, we consider on the parity of k.

114

- If k is even, then $k = 2m$ for some $m \in \mathbb{Z}$. Hence,

$$\left[\frac{k}{2}\right] + \left[\frac{k+1}{2}\right] = \left[\frac{2m}{2}\right] + \left[\frac{2m+1}{2}\right]$$

$$= [m] + \left[\frac{2m}{2} + \frac{1}{2}\right]$$

$$= [m] + \left[m + \frac{1}{2}\right]$$

$$= m + m$$

$$= 2m = k$$

- If k is odd, then $k = 2m + 1$ for some $m \in \mathbb{Z}$. Then

$$\left[\frac{k}{2}\right] + \left[\frac{k+1}{2}\right] = \left[\frac{2m+1}{2}\right] + \left[\frac{2m+1+1}{2}\right]$$

$$= \left[\frac{2m}{2} + \frac{1}{2}\right] + \left[\frac{2(m+1)}{2}\right]$$

$$= \left[m + \frac{1}{2}\right] + [m + 1]$$

$$= m + m + 1$$

$$= 2m + 1 = k.$$

Therefore, $\left[\dfrac{k}{2}\right] + \left[\dfrac{k+1}{2}\right] = k.$

2. Compute $S = \left[\dfrac{1}{2}\right] + \left[\dfrac{2}{2}\right] + ... + \left[\dfrac{n}{2}\right]$.

We have

$$S = \left[\frac{1}{2}\right] + \left[\frac{2}{2}\right] + ... + \left[\frac{n-1}{2}\right] + \left[\frac{n}{2}\right]$$

$$= \left[\frac{1}{2}\right] + \left(\left[\frac{2}{2}\right] + ... + \left[\frac{n-1}{2}\right] + \left[\frac{n}{2}\right]\right).$$

S also can be written as

$$S = \left(\left[\frac{1}{2}\right] + \left[\frac{2}{2}\right] + ... + \left[\frac{n-1}{2}\right]\right) + \left[\frac{n}{2}\right].$$

Then

$$2S = \left[\frac{1}{2}\right] + \left(\left[\frac{1}{2}\right] + \left[\frac{2}{2}\right]\right) + \dots + \left(\left[\frac{n-1}{2}\right] + \left[\frac{n}{2}\right]\right) + \left[\frac{n}{2}\right].$$

From the above proof, we have $\left[\dfrac{k}{2}\right] + \left[\dfrac{k+1}{2}\right] = k$ for all positive integers k. Hence,

$$2S = \left[\frac{1}{2}\right] + 1 + 2 + \dots + (n-1) + \left[\frac{n}{2}\right]$$
$$= \frac{n(n-1)}{2} + \left[\frac{n}{2}\right].$$

$$\boxed{\text{Therefore, } S = \frac{n(n-1)}{4} + \frac{1}{2}\left[\frac{n}{2}\right].}$$

Problem 166. Suppose that a and b are two real numbers that satisfy $0 \le a - b \le 1$. Prove that $[a] - [b] \in \{0, 1\}$.

Solution. Prove that $[a] - [b] \in \{0, 1\}$
By the definition of integer part, we have

$$a - 1 < [a] \le a. \tag{1}$$

Similarly, $b - 1 < [b] \le b$.
We obtain

$$-b \le -[b] < -b + 1. \tag{2}$$

Adding (1) and (2), it follows that

$$a - b - 1 < [a] - [b] < a - b + 1.$$

Since $0 \le a - b \le 1$, we obtain

$$0 - 1 < [a] - [b] < 1 + 1.$$

Hence, $-1 < [a] - [b] < 2$.
Moreover, $[a] - [b]$ is and integer.

$$\boxed{\text{Therefore, } [a] - [b] \in \{0, 1\}.}$$

Remark 3. For all positive integers k, we have

$$\sqrt{k+1} - \sqrt{k} = \frac{\left(\sqrt{k+1} - \sqrt{k}\right)\left(\sqrt{k+1} + \sqrt{k}\right)}{\sqrt{k+1} + \sqrt{k}}$$

$$= \frac{\sqrt{(k+1)^2} - \sqrt{k^2}}{\sqrt{k+1} + \sqrt{k}}$$

$$= \frac{k+1-k}{\sqrt{k+1} + \sqrt{k}}$$

$$= \frac{1}{\sqrt{k+1} + \sqrt{k}} < 1$$

since $\sqrt{k+1} + \sqrt{k} > 1$.

From the above problem, we obtain $\left[\sqrt{k+1}\right] - \left[\sqrt{k}\right] \in \{0, 1\}$.

Similarly, we have $\left[\sqrt[n]{k+1}\right] - \left[\sqrt[n]{k}\right] \in \{0, 1\}$ for all $n \geq 2$.

Moreover, for all $m \geq 2$, we obtain

$$\log_m (k+1) - \log_m k = \log_m \left(\frac{k+1}{k}\right)$$

$$= \log_m \left(1 + \frac{1}{k}\right)$$

$$\leq \log_m 2$$

$$\leq \log_m m = 1.$$

From the above problem, we obtain

$$[\log_m (k+1)] - [\log_m k] \in \{0, 1\}.$$

The property in the above remark will be used to solve the following problem.

Problem 167. Let $S_n = 1^m + 2^m + ... + n^m$, where $m \geq 2$ is a positive integer. Find $T_m = \left[\sqrt[m]{1}\right] + \left[\sqrt[m]{2}\right] + ... + \left[\sqrt[m]{n}\right]$ in terms of $\left[\sqrt[m]{n}\right]$ and $S_{\left[\sqrt[m]{n}\right]}$. Then find T_2 and T_3.

Solution. We begin by proving the following lemma:

Lemma 5. Given that $\{x_n\}$ is a sequence of real number. Then the sum of the first n terms of $\{x_n\}$ is given by

$$S_n = nx_n - \sum_{k=1}^{n-1} k(x_{k+1} - x_k).$$

117

Proof. We have

$$nx_n - \sum_{k=1}^{n-1} k\left(x_{k+1} - x_k\right)$$

$$= nx_n - \sum_{k=1}^{n-1} \left(kx_{k+1} - kx_k\right)$$

$$= nx_n - \sum_{k=1}^{n-1} \left(kx_{k+1} - (k-1)x_k - x_k\right)$$

$$= nx_n - \sum_{k=1}^{n-1} \left(kx_{k+1} - (k-1)x_k\right) + \sum_{k=1}^{n-1} x_k$$

$$= nx_n - (n-1)x_n + \sum_{k=1}^{n-1} x_k$$

$$= x_n + \sum_{k=1}^{n-1} x_k$$

$$= x_n + x_{n-1} + \dots + x_2 + x_1$$

$$= S_n.$$

Therefore, $S_n = nx_n - \sum_{k=1}^{n-1} k\left(x_{k+1} - x_k\right).$ $\qquad\square$

Let $\{x_n\} : \left[\sqrt[m]{1}\right], \left[\sqrt[m]{2}\right], \dots, \left[\sqrt[m]{n}\right].$

Then $T_m = nx_n - \sum_{k=1}^{n-1} k\left(x_{k+1} - x_k\right).$

We have $x_{k+1} - x_k \in \{0, 1\}.$

If $x_{k+1} - x_k \neq 0$, then there exists an integer a such that

$$\sqrt[m]{k} < a \le \sqrt[m]{k+1}.$$

It follows that $k < a^m \le k+1$. Hence, $k = a^m - 1$.

For $k \le n-1$, we obtain $a^m - 1 \le n-1$.

Then $a \le \sqrt[m]{n}$. It implies that

$$T_m = n\left[\sqrt[m]{n}\right] - \sum_{a=1}^{\left[\sqrt[m]{n}\right]} \left(a^m - 1\right) \times 1$$

118

$$= n \left[\sqrt[m]{n} \right] - \sum_{a=1}^{\left[\sqrt[m]{n} \right]} a^m + \sum_{a=1}^{\left[\sqrt[m]{n} \right]} 1$$

$$= n \left[\sqrt[m]{n} \right] - S_{\left[\sqrt[m]{n} \right]} + \left[\sqrt[m]{n} \right]$$

$$= (n+1) \left[\sqrt[m]{n} \right] - S_{\left[\sqrt[m]{n} \right]}.$$

Therefore, $T_m = (n+1) \left[\sqrt[m]{n} \right] - S_{\left[\sqrt[m]{n} \right]}.$

For $m = 2$, we obtain

$$T_2 = (n+1) \left[\sqrt{n} \right] - S_{\left[\sqrt{n} \right]}$$

$$= (n+1) \left[\sqrt{n} \right] - \left(1^2 + 2^2 + \ldots + \left[\sqrt{n} \right]^2 \right)$$

$$= (n+1) \left[\sqrt{n} \right] - \frac{\left[\sqrt{n} \right] \left(\left[\sqrt{n} \right] + 1 \right) \left(2 \left[\sqrt{n} \right] + 1 \right)}{6}.$$

Therefore, $T_2 = (n+1) \left[\sqrt{n} \right] - \dfrac{\left[\sqrt{n} \right] \left(\left[\sqrt{n} \right] + 1 \right) \left(2 \left[\sqrt{n} \right] + 1 \right)}{6}.$

For $n = 3$, it follows that

$$T_3 = (n+1) \left[\sqrt[3]{n} \right] - S_{\left[\sqrt[3]{n} \right]}$$

$$= (n+1) \left[\sqrt[3]{n} \right] - \left(1^3 + 2^3 + \ldots + \left[\sqrt[3]{n} \right]^3 \right)$$

$$= (n+1) \left[\sqrt[3]{n} \right] - \left(\frac{\left[\sqrt[3]{n} \right] \left(\left[\sqrt[3]{n} \right] + 1 \right)}{2} \right)^2$$

$$= (n+1) \left[\sqrt[3]{n} \right] - \frac{\left[\sqrt[3]{n} \right]^2 \left(\left[\sqrt[3]{n} \right] + 1 \right)^2}{4}.$$

Therefore, $T_3 = (n+1) \left[\sqrt[3]{n} \right] - \dfrac{\left[\sqrt[3]{n} \right]^2 \left(\left[\sqrt[3]{n} \right] + 1 \right)^2}{4}.$

Problem 168. Compute $S_{m,n} = [\log_m 1] + [\log_m 2] + \ldots + [\log_m n]$ in terms of $[\log_m n]$. In the above notation, $m \geq 2$ and n are positive integers.

Solution. Compute $S_{m,n}$.

Let $\{x_n\} : [\log_m 1], [\log_m 2], \ldots, [\log_m n]$.

We obtain $S_{m,n} = n x_n - \sum_{k=1}^{n-1} k \left(x_{k+1} - x_k \right).$

119

We have $[\log_m(k+1)] - [\log_m k] \in \{0,1\}$.

If $[\log_m(k+1)] - [\log_m k] \neq 0$, then there exists an integer a such that

$$\log_m k < a \leq \log_m(k+1).$$

It follows that $k < m^a \leq k+1$.

Hence, $k = m^a - 1$.

If $k \leq n-1$, we obtain $m^a - 1 \leq n-1$.

Then $a \leq \log_m n$.

It implies that

$$S_{m,n} = n[\log_m n] - \sum_{a=1}^{[\log_m n]}(m^a - 1)$$

$$= n[\log_m n] - \sum_{a=1}^{[\log_m n]} m^a + \sum_{a=1}^{[\log_m n]} 1$$

$$= n[\log_m n] - \frac{m\left(m^{[\log_m n]} - 1\right)}{m-1} + [\log_m n]$$

$$= (n+1)[\log_m n] - \frac{m\left(m^{[\log_m n]} - 1\right)}{m-1}.$$

Therefore, $S_{m,n} = (n+1)[\log_m n] - \dfrac{m\left(m^{[\log_m n]} - 1\right)}{m-1}.$

Problem 169. Let x be a real number and n be a positive integer. Prove that

$$[x] + [x + \{x\}] + [2x + \{2x\}] + \dots + [2nx + \{2nx\}] = [4nx].$$

Solution. Prove that

$$[x] + [x + \{x\}] + [2x + \{2x\}] + \dots + [2nx + \{2nx\}] = [4nx].$$

By the definition of integer part, we have $y = \{y\} + [y]$ for all real number y. Then

$$[y + \{y\}] = [2y - y + \{y\}]$$
$$= [2y - (y - \{y\})]$$
$$= [2y - [y]]$$
$$= [2y] - [y].$$

Substitute y by $x, 2x, 4x, ...,$ and $2nx$, we obtain

$$[x + \{x\}] = [2x] - [x];$$
$$[2x + \{2x\}] = [4x] - [2x];$$
$$[3x + \{3x\}] = [6x] - [4x];$$

$$\vdots$$

and $\quad [2nx + \{2nx\}] = [4nx] - [2nx].$

Adding all of the above equalities, we obtain

$$[x + \{x\}] + [2x + \{2x\}] + ... + [2nx + \{2nx\}] = [4nx] - [x].$$

Therefore, the identity is proved.

Problem 170. Given x is a real number and n is a positive integer. Prove that

$$n(2[x] - 1) \le \left[x - \frac{1}{n}\right] + \left[x - \frac{1}{n-1}\right] + ... + \left[x + \frac{1}{n-1}\right] + \left[x + \frac{1}{n}\right]$$
$$\le n(2[x] + 1).$$

Solution. Prove that
$$n(2[x] - 1) \le \left[x - \frac{1}{n}\right] + \left[x - \frac{1}{n-1}\right] + ... + \left[x + \frac{1}{n-1}\right]$$
$$+ \left[x + \frac{1}{n}\right] \le n(2[x] + 1).$$
We begin by proving the following lemma:

Lemma 6. Given x is a real number and k is a positive integer. Then

$$n(2[x] - 1) \le \left[x - \frac{1}{n}\right] + \left[x - \frac{1}{n-1}\right] + ... + \left[x + \frac{1}{n-1}\right] + \left[x + \frac{1}{n}\right]$$
$$\le n(2[x] + 1).$$

Proof. By the definition of integer part, we have $x = [x] + \{x\}$. Then

$$\left[x - \frac{1}{k}\right] + \left[x + \frac{1}{k}\right] = \left[[x] + \{x\} - \frac{1}{k}\right] + \left[[x] + \{x\} + \frac{1}{k}\right]$$

$$= [x] + \left[\{x\} - \frac{1}{k}\right] + [x] + \left[\{x\} + \frac{1}{k}\right]$$

121

$$= 2\left[x\right] + \left[\{x\} - \frac{1}{k}\right] + \left[\{x\} + \frac{1}{k}\right].$$

Since $0 \le \{x\} < 1$, we obtain

$$-1 \le -\frac{1}{k} \le \{x\} - \frac{1}{k} < 1 - \frac{1}{k} < 1$$

and

$$\frac{1}{k} \le \{x\} + \frac{1}{k} < 1 + \frac{1}{k} \le 2.$$

It follows that $-1 \le \left[\{x\} - \frac{1}{k}\right] \le 0$ and $0 \le \left[\{x\} + \frac{1}{k}\right] \le 1$.
It implies that

$$-1 \le \left[\{x\} - \frac{1}{k}\right] + \left[\{x\} + \frac{1}{k}\right] \le 1.$$

We obtain

$$2\left[x\right] - 1 \le \left[2x\right] + \left[\{x\} - \frac{1}{k}\right] + \left[\{x\} + \frac{1}{k}\right] \le 2\left[x\right] + 1.$$

Then

$$2\left[x\right] - 1 \le \left[x - \frac{1}{k}\right] + \left[x + \frac{1}{k}\right] \le 2\left[x\right] + 1.$$

Thus, the lemma is proved. □

From the above lemma, we have

$$2\left[x\right] - 1 \le \left[x - \frac{1}{k}\right] + \left[x + \frac{1}{k}\right] \le 2\left[x\right] + 1$$

for all real number x and positive integer k.
Let $k = 1, 2, ..., n$. We obtain

$$2\left[x\right] - 1 \le \left[x - 1\right] + \left[x + 1\right] \le 2\left[x\right] + 1;$$

$$2\left[x\right] - 1 \le \left[x - \frac{1}{2}\right] + \left[x + \frac{1}{2}\right] \le 2\left[x\right] + 1;$$

$$\vdots$$

and $2\left[x\right] - 1 \le \left[x - \frac{1}{n}\right] + \left[x + \frac{1}{n}\right] \le 2\left[x\right] + 1.$

Adding all of the above inequalities, we obtain

$$n\left(2\left[x\right]-1\right)\leq\left[x-\frac{1}{n}\right]+\left[x-\frac{1}{n-1}\right]+...+\left[x+\frac{1}{n-1}\right]+\left[x+\frac{1}{n}\right]$$

$$\leq n\left(2\left[x\right]+1\right).$$

Therefore, the inequality is proved.

Problem 171.   1. (Hermite's identity)

Given x is a real number and n is a positive integer. Prove that

$$[nx] = [x] + \left[x+\frac{1}{n}\right] + \left[x+\frac{2}{n}\right] + ... + \left[x+\frac{n-1}{n}\right].$$

2. Find S which is defined by

$$S = \left[x+\frac{1}{2}\right] + \left[2x+\frac{1}{2}\right] + ... + \left[2^n x+\frac{1}{2}\right].$$

3. For all real number x, prove that

$$\{x\}+\left\{x+\frac{1}{n}\right\}+\left\{x+\frac{2}{n}\right\}+...+\left\{x+\frac{n-1}{n}\right\} = \{nx\}+\frac{n-1}{2}.$$

Solution.   1. Prove that

$$[nx] = [x] + \left[x+\frac{1}{n}\right] + \left[x+\frac{2}{n}\right] + ... + \left[x+\frac{n-1}{n}\right].$$

If x is an integer, we obtain

$$[x] + \left[x+\frac{1}{n}\right] + \left[x+\frac{2}{n}\right] + ... + \left[x+\frac{n-1}{n}\right]$$

$$= \underbrace{x + x + ... + x}_{n}$$

$$= nx$$

and $[nx] = nx$.
In this case, we obtain

$$[nx] = [x] + \left[x+\frac{1}{n}\right] + \left[x+\frac{2}{n}\right] + ... + \left[x+\frac{n-1}{n}\right].$$

For $1 \le i \le n$, we obtain

$$\left[x + \frac{i}{n}\right] = \left[[x] + \{x\} + \frac{i}{n}\right] = [x] + \left[\{x\} + \frac{i}{n}\right].$$

By knowing that $0 \le \{x\} < 1$, we obtain

$$0 < \frac{i}{n} \le \{x\} + \frac{i}{n} < 1 + \frac{i}{n} < 2.$$

Then $\left[\{x\} + \dfrac{i}{n}\right] \in \{0, 1\}$.

It follows that

$$[x] \le \left[x + \frac{1}{n}\right] \le \left[x + \frac{2}{n}\right] \le \ldots \le \left[x + \frac{n-1}{n}\right] \le [x] + 1.$$

From $\dfrac{i}{n} \le \{x\} + \dfrac{i}{n} < 1 + \dfrac{i}{n} < 2$, if $i, 0 \le i \le n-1$, we obtain

$$\frac{i}{n} \le \{x\} + \frac{i}{n} < 1.$$

Then $0 \le \{x\} < 1 - \dfrac{i}{n}$.

It follows that $0 \le n\{x\} < n - i$ for all $i = \overline{1, n-1}$.

We obtain $0 \le n\{x\} < 1$.

Hence, $[n\{x\}] = 0$.

It follows that

$$\begin{aligned}
[nx] &= [n([x] + \{x\})] \\
&= [n[x] + n\{x\}] \\
&= n[x] + [n\{x\}] \\
&= n[x] + 0 \\
&= n[x].
\end{aligned}$$

Moreover,

$$[x] + \left[x + \frac{1}{n}\right] + \left[x + \frac{2}{n}\right] + \ldots + \left[x + \frac{n-1}{n}\right]$$

$$= \underbrace{[x] + [x] + \ldots + [x]}_{n}$$

$$= n[x].$$

We obtain $[nx] = [x] + \left[x + \dfrac{1}{n}\right] + \left[x + \dfrac{2}{n}\right] + ... + \left[x + \dfrac{n-1}{n}\right].$

There is only one remaining case to prove. It is the case when there exists an integer i such that $i, 0 \le i \le n-1$, where

$$1 \le \{x\} + \frac{i}{n}$$

and

$$\{x\} + \frac{i-1}{n} < 1.$$

We obtain

$$[x] = \left[x + \frac{1}{n}\right] = ... = \left[x + \frac{i-1}{n}\right]$$

and

$$\left[x + \frac{i}{n}\right] = \left[x + \frac{i+1}{n}\right] = ... = \left[x + \frac{n-1}{n}\right] = [x] + 1.$$

It implies that

$$[x] + \left[x + \frac{1}{n}\right] + \left[x + \frac{2}{n}\right] + ... + \left[x + \frac{n-1}{n}\right]$$
$$= i\,[x] + (n-i)\,([x]+1)$$
$$= i\,[x] + n\,[x] + n - i\,[x] - i$$
$$= n\,[x] + n - i. \tag{1}$$

From $1 \le \{x\} + \dfrac{i}{n}$ and $\{x\} + \dfrac{i-1}{n} < 1$, we obtain

$$n - i \le n\{x\} < n - i + 1.$$

Then $n\,[x] + n - i \le n\{x\} + n\,[x] < n\,[x] + n - i + 1$.
It follows that $n\,[x] + n - i \le nx < n\,[x] + n - i + 1$.
Hence,

$$[nx] = n\,[x] + n - i. \tag{2}$$

From (1) and (2), we obtain

$$[nx] = [x] + \left[x + \frac{1}{n}\right] + \left[x + \frac{2}{n}\right] + ... + \left[x + \frac{n-1}{n}\right].$$

Therefore, the identity is proved.

2. Compute $S = \left[x + \dfrac{1}{2}\right] + \left[2x + \dfrac{1}{2}\right] + \ldots + \left[2^n x + \dfrac{1}{2}\right]$.

Using Hermite's identity, for $n = 2$, we obtain

$$[2x] = [x] + \left[x + \frac{1}{2}\right].$$

It follows that $\left[x + \dfrac{1}{2}\right] = [2x] - [x]$.

Similarly, we obtain

$$\left[2x + \frac{1}{2}\right] = [2^2 x] - [2x];$$

$$\left[2^2 x + \frac{1}{2}\right] = [2^3 x] - [2^2 x];$$

$$\vdots$$

and $\quad \left[2^n x + \dfrac{1}{2}\right] = [2^{n+1} x] - [2^n x]$.

Adding all of the above equalities, we obtain

$$S = [2^{n+1} x] - [x].$$

Therefore, $S = [2^{n+1} x] - [x]$.

3. Prove that $\{x\} + \left\{x + \dfrac{1}{n}\right\} + \left\{x + \dfrac{2}{n}\right\} + \ldots + \left\{x + \dfrac{n-1}{n}\right\}$

$$= \{nx\} + \frac{n-1}{2}.$$

Since $\{x\} = x - [x]$, we obtain

$$\{x\} + \left\{x + \frac{1}{n}\right\} + \left\{x + \frac{2}{n}\right\} + \ldots + \left\{x + \frac{n-1}{n}\right\}$$

$$= x - [x] + x + \frac{1}{n} - \left[x + \frac{1}{n}\right] + \ldots + x + \frac{n-1}{n} - \left[x + \frac{n-1}{n}\right]$$

$$= nx + \frac{1 + 2 + \ldots + (n-1)}{n}$$

$$- \left([x] + \left[x + \frac{1}{n}\right] + \ldots + \left[x + \frac{n-1}{n}\right]\right)$$

$$= nx + \frac{\frac{n(n-1)}{2}}{n} - [nx]$$

$$= nx - [nx] + \frac{n-1}{2}$$

$$= \{nx\} + \frac{n-1}{2}.$$

> Therefore, $\{x\} + \left\{x + \dfrac{1}{n}\right\} + \left\{x + \dfrac{2}{n}\right\} + \ldots + \left\{x + \dfrac{n-1}{n}\right\}$
>
> $$= \{nx\} + \frac{n-1}{2}.$$

Problem 172. Given $x \notin \mathbb{N}$ is a positive real number and $n \geq 2$ is a positive integer. Assume that $\dfrac{1}{\{x\}} \leq n$. Prove that

$$[x] + \left[x + \frac{1}{2}\right] + \left[x + \frac{2}{3}\right] + \ldots + \left[x + \frac{n-1}{n}\right] = n[x] + n - \left[\frac{1}{\{x\}}\right] + \sigma$$

, where $\sigma = \begin{cases} 1 & \text{if } \dfrac{1}{\{x\}} \in \mathbb{N} \\ 0 & \text{if } \dfrac{1}{\{x\}} \notin \mathbb{N} \end{cases}$.

1. Compute $S = [1.2] + \left[1.2 + \dfrac{1}{2}\right] + \left[1.2 + \dfrac{2}{3}\right] + \ldots + \left[1.2 + \dfrac{99}{100}\right]$.

2. Given $x \notin \mathbb{N}$ is a positive real number such that

$$\frac{1}{\{x\}}, \frac{1}{\{x + 0.5\}} \leq 2.$$

Let n be a positive integer. Prove that

$$\left[\frac{1}{\{x\}}\right] + \left[\frac{1}{\{x + 0.5\}}\right] + \ldots + \left[\frac{1}{\{x + 0.5n\}}\right]$$
$$= [x] - \left[x + \frac{n+1}{2}\right] + (\sigma + 2)(n + 1).$$

Solution.   1. Prove that

$$[x] + \left[x + \frac{1}{2}\right] + \left[x + \frac{2}{3}\right] + \ldots + \left[x + \frac{n-1}{n}\right]$$

127

$$= n\left[x\right] + n - \left[\frac{1}{\{x\}}\right] + \sigma.$$

For all real numbers y, we have $y = [y] + \{y\}$.
Then

$$[x] + \left[x + \frac{1}{2}\right] + \left[x + \frac{2}{3}\right] + \ldots + \left[x + \frac{n-1}{n}\right]$$

$$= [x] + \left[[x] + \{x\} + \frac{1}{2}\right] + \left[[x] + \{x\} + \frac{2}{3}\right] + \ldots$$

$$+ \left[[x] + \{x\} + \frac{n-1}{n}\right]$$

$$= [x] + [x] + \left[\{x\} + \frac{1}{2}\right] + [x] + \left[\{x\} + \frac{2}{3}\right] + \ldots$$

$$+ [x] + \left[\{x\} + \frac{n-1}{n}\right]$$

$$= \underbrace{[x] + [x] + \ldots + [x]}_{n} + \left[\{x\} + \frac{1}{2}\right] + \left[\{x\} + \frac{2}{3}\right] + \ldots$$

$$+ \left[\{x\} + \frac{n-1}{n}\right]$$

$$= n[x] + \left[\{x\} + \frac{1}{2}\right] + \left[\{x\} + \frac{2}{3}\right] + \ldots + \left[\{x\} + \frac{n-1}{n}\right].$$

Since $\dfrac{1}{\{x\}} \leq n$, we obtain $\{x\} \geq \dfrac{1}{n}$.
It follows that $\{x\} + \dfrac{i}{i+1} \geq \dfrac{1}{n} + \dfrac{i}{i+1}$.
For $i = n-1$, we obtain

$$\{x\} + \frac{i}{i+1} \geq \frac{1}{n} + \frac{n-1}{n-1+1} = \frac{n}{n} = 1.$$

It turns out that we always can find $0 \leq k \leq n-1$ such that

$$\{x\} + \frac{k-1}{k} < 1$$

and

$$\{x\} + \frac{k}{k+1} \geq 1.$$

From the last two inequalities, we obtain $\dfrac{1}{\{x\}} - 1 \le k < \dfrac{1}{\{x\}}$.

Then $k = \left[\dfrac{1}{\{x\}}\right] - \sigma$.

Hence,

$$[x] + \left[x + \frac{1}{2}\right] + \left[x + \frac{2}{3}\right] + \ldots + \left[x + \frac{n-1}{n}\right]$$
$$= n\,[x] + \underbrace{0 + 0 + \ldots + 0}_{k-1} + \underbrace{1 + 1 + \ldots + 1}_{n-k}$$
$$= n\,[x] + n - k$$
$$= n\,[x] + n - \left(\left[\frac{1}{\{x\}}\right] - \sigma\right)$$
$$= n\,[x] + n - \left[\frac{1}{\{x\}}\right] + \sigma.$$

Therefore, $[x] + \left[x + \dfrac{1}{2}\right] + \left[x + \dfrac{2}{3}\right] + \ldots + \left[x + \dfrac{n-1}{n}\right]$

$$= n\,[x] + n - \left[\frac{1}{\{x\}}\right] + \sigma.$$

2. Compute $S = [1.2] + \left[1.2 + \dfrac{1}{2}\right] + \left[1.2 + \dfrac{2}{3}\right] + \ldots + \left[1.2 + \dfrac{99}{100}\right]$.

Compare the given sum to the identity in (1), we obtain $x = 1.2, n = 100$. Then $\{x\} = \{1.2\} = 0.2$.

It follows that $\dfrac{1}{\{x\}} = \dfrac{1}{0.2} = 5 < 100$.

Hence, $\sigma = 1$.

It implies that

$$S = n\,[x] + n - \left[\frac{1}{\{x\}}\right] + \sigma$$
$$= 100\,[1.2] + 100 - [5] + 1$$
$$= 100 + 100 - 5 + 1$$
$$= 196.$$

Therefore, $S = 196$.

3. Prove that $\left[\dfrac{1}{\{x\}}\right] + \left[\dfrac{1}{\{x+0.5\}}\right] + \ldots + \left[\dfrac{1}{\{x+0.5n\}}\right]$

$$= [x] - \left[x + \dfrac{n+1}{2}\right] + (\sigma + 2)(n+1).$$

We have $[x] + \left[x + \dfrac{1}{2}\right] + \left[x + \dfrac{2}{3}\right] + \ldots + \left[x + \dfrac{n-1}{n}\right]$

$$= n\,[x] + n - \left[\dfrac{1}{\{x\}}\right] + \sigma.$$

For $k = 2$ and $\dfrac{1}{\{x\}}, \dfrac{1}{\{x+0.5\}} \le 2$, it follows that

$$[x] + \left[x + \dfrac{1}{2}\right] = 2\,[x] + 2 - \left[\dfrac{1}{\{x\}}\right] + \sigma.$$

Then $\left[\dfrac{1}{\{x\}}\right] = [x] - [x + 0.5] + 2 + \sigma.$

Similarly, we obtain

$$\left[\dfrac{1}{\{x+0.5\}}\right] = [x + 0.5] - [x + 1] + 2 + \sigma;$$

$$\left[\dfrac{1}{\{x+1\}}\right] = [x + 1] - [x + 1.5] + 2 + \sigma;$$

$$\vdots$$

and $\left[\dfrac{1}{\{x+0.5n\}}\right] = [x + 0.5n] - [x + 0.5\,(n+1)] + 2 + \sigma.$

Adding all of the above equalities, we obtain

$$\left[\dfrac{1}{\{x\}}\right] + \left[\dfrac{1}{\{x+0.5\}}\right] + \ldots + \left[\dfrac{1}{\{x+0.5n\}}\right]$$

$$= [x] - \left[x + \dfrac{n+1}{2}\right] + 2(n+1) + \sigma(n+1)$$

Therefore, $\left[\dfrac{1}{\{x\}}\right] + \left[\dfrac{1}{\{x+0.5\}}\right] + \ldots + \left[\dfrac{1}{\{x+0.5n\}}\right]$

$$= [x] - \left[x + \dfrac{n+1}{2}\right] + (\sigma + 2)(n+1).$$

Made in the USA
Monee, IL
08 January 2025